Eat with joy—on a wheat-
free, gluten-free diet

'Man did not weave the web of life, he is merely a strand in it, whatever he does to the web, he does to himself.'

American Chief Seattle

Eat With Joy

on a wheat-free, gluten-free diet

Ann O'Dowd Fogarty

A. & A. Farmar

British Library cataloguing in Publication Data
A CIP catalogue record for this book is available from the
British Library

Cover design by Cobalt
Cover photograph courtesy of Bord Bia
Text designed and set by A. & A. Farmar
Printed and bound by GraphyCems
Index by Helen Litton

ISBN 1-899047-73-5

First published in 2001
by
A. & A. Farmar
Beech House
78 Ranelagh Village
Dublin 6
Ireland
Tel: +353 1 496 3625
Fax: + 353 1 497 0107
Email: afarmar@iol.ie
Web: farmarbooks.com

To Mary, Seán, Edmond and Amy
with light and love

Contents

Acknowledgements

I would like to express my love and gratitude to all who supported and encouraged me in all sorts of ways while writing this book, especially my husband Ed. Special thanks to Mary Finlay, Paula O'Regan, Ann Sharples, and Seán O'Brien for permission to use their photographs.

Love and thanks to Marie not only for her love and support but for very valuable feedback on sampling some recipes, and to Catherine with whom I was always happy to go walking by Wicklow Bay to get a break from the book—bless your heart Catherine!

Go méadaí Dia bhúr stór.

'May the light of your soul guide you to perfect health.'

Introduction

Writing this book was not a decision I arrived at overnight or out of the blue. The book has been in the making since I was a little girl when, with my 'Meta'-powered toy stove, I prepared and cooked the 'dinner' by my mother's side at the kitchen table. With the ingredients that she was using—bits of cabbage, sugar, flour, sour milk, water or anything else that I could get my hands on—and following my very own creative recipes, I prepared and cooked dinner in my little saucepans. My mother, Mary, is the best cook that I know and from her I learned a great appreciation of good food and a passion for cookery. My late father, Seán, when he said in one of his more undiplomatic moments that I was a better cook than my mother, was quickly reminded which side his bread was buttered! So, to Mary, Seán, and to my husband, Edmond, who gives me every support and encouragement and who has been acting as guinea pig over the past two years, I dedicate this work.

At this point in my life I have come to understand that there is a potential for growth in all of life's experiences especially the more difficult. As a child I suffered greatly from pains in my tummy. I learned to put up and live with them. As I grew older the pains became worse and even more persistent. I was told that I had irritable bowel syndrome and I was given medication which didn't work. A growing awareness of alternative medicine and its philosophy led me to seek a solution to my problem in that field. One practitioner told me that I was allergic to more than fifteen different foods. Most of these allergies were slight, apart from dairy and wheat, and I had to give up those products. When I had established what was causing my pain, the solution placed another stress on me! For one who liked her food, a diet without wheat and dairy foods was especially difficult and I worried how I might cook without these foods yet be properly nourished and satisfied. It surprised me, as someone who enjoyed cooking so much, that being placed on such a diet could be so stressful and difficult. As I was constantly associating certain foods with pain, I began to look at food in a very negative way. However, even though I lost a lot of weight on the dairy and wheat-free diet and looked pretty miserable, I improved almost immediately and

1

my bouts of pain occurred less often.

This experience fuelled my interest in the relationship between food and healing and led me to study for a Diploma in Nutrition. My studies awakened in me an awareness of the life force and the holistic approach to health which involves body, mind and spirit. (At the end of this book I have given you a reading list that was, and still is, extremely helpful to me on my journey, in the hope that it will be of help to you too.) Around this time, a most caring, gifted and compassionate woman, who has become a very dear friend, came into my life. She, Marcella, is a health care practitioner who works in the alternative health field. I am so grateful to her as she enabled me to free myself from the diet and live a normal life again. I now enjoy all good food without any ill effects and I am much better able to cope with life and all its stresses. Before I share some of Marcella's wisdom with you, let me tell you a little of my understanding of the importance of organic food and the nature of the life force.

As nature intended

We are an integral part of nature. When our practices are in harmony with nature, we create harmony in the body. On the other hand, destructive practices can lead to suffering not only for nature but also for humankind. To bring about healing and to maintain a state of health, we need to select the freshest and cleanest possible food for consumption. This is food that is grown with respect for the laws of nature. Fresh organic food, properly prepared, is the ideal. It has a strong life force of its own and is packed with vitamins and minerals. Grown without the use of chemicals, organic food, apart from naturally occurring toxins, is toxin-free. We should avoid convenience food as far as possible as, by its very nature, it demands the use of additives, most of which are not desirable. It is highly processed and for that reason is vitamin- and mineral-deficient and lacking in any life force. Many processed foods also contain high amounts of added salt, sugar and fat. If you have to eat convenience food, make sure that it is from the quality end of the market and that you always read the labels. 'You get what you pay for' is especially true for convenience food.

A word about the life force (prana or ki)

The life force, or vital force as it is sometimes called, enters the body at conception. It keeps the body alive and healthy and leaves at the time of death. During life the body can repair itself through the prana or vital force. We take it into our bodies from sunlight, air, ground, water and fresh food. Positive life practices prevent prana (life force) from leaking out of the body. A vibrant life force results in a person who is healthy in body, mind and spirit. It leads to good digestion, absorption and assimilation of food. As a result, the cells of our bodies have all the building blocks they need for their efficient working and health. A strong life force also causes the waste products of metabolism, and the toxins which we take into our bodies, to be easily eliminated and not allowed to accumulate. The accumulation of toxins in the body leads to a weakening of the life force and consequent disease. When nutrients are absorbed and assimilated well and toxins are thrown off, the blood and lymph remain healthy and nourish the tissues with the correct nutrients in terms of quality and quantity. This in turn keeps the life force strong and in balance. All factors are interdependent: vibrant life force, good digestion, absorption and assimilation of food, and good quality lymph and blood. On the other hand, weakened life force leads to the opposite. The body is unable to get hold of sufficient nutrients and to get rid of toxins. This results in the blood and lymph becoming unhealthy and unable to nourish the tissues as they should; there is an accumulation of poisons in the cells and this gives rise to chronic illness. When stress, unease or conflict overwhelms us, our toxic burden is greatly increased and this depletes the life force even further. Therefore it is not sufficient to attend solely to bodily needs to strengthen the life force and bring about healing, it is equally necessary to attend to mental and spiritual needs.

To strengthen your life force

Now I share with you what I have learned from my wonderful and gifted friend, Marcella. As well as attention to your diet, cultivate the following life practices so as to strengthen your life force.

1. Most of us are in a dream world most of the time and need to wake up. Always be in the moment, giving total attention to each thing that you are doing as you are doing it. In other words: no day dreaming! If and when you need to work things out, do so consciously. By living only in the now, you will eliminate many fears and stresses from your life. Life force is depleted by not being in the moment. By being present you will become far more efficient, you will be far more centred, far calmer, much more aware, more patient and more loving to those around you. When in the moment you will also be amazed both by how your life is being supported and directed and by the many miracles happening all around you.

2. Practise meditation each day. Meditation has spiritual, physical and mental benefits. It is a wonderful way of achieving calmness and centredness so that the higher self rather than the ego directs you. Getting in touch with the real you

allows you to put love rather than judgement into your relationships with others. It allows you to love unconditionally freeing both yourself and the other to make the best possible choices for your mutual growth. Your heart rather than your head will guide you so that you will become more intuitive. On a physical level, meditation regulates blood pressure, helps to reduce cholesterol, and improves memory and concentration.

3. Let go of grief, anger, obsession, fear and guilt. Holding on depletes your life force. Let go of everything that disturbs you and be in the present. If you are a believer: let go and let God. Put into practice forgiveness and letting go in order to release yourself from destructive ways of thinking and to bring about instead health of body, mind and spirit. When you come up against a difficulty, do your best, and if things still don't work out as you would like, let go in the certain knowledge that there is a greater power directing your life and something better than you had planned is in store for you. You will be surprised at the miracles happening in your life when you begin to practise this. Look on the sufferings, sorrows, disappointments and difficulties of life as gifts which are opportunities for change and growth. Of course, there are times when we would wish that circumstances and people were different but though we cannot change them, we can change our reaction to them.

4. Make sure that there is lots of joy in your life. Make decisions to be happy and do not allow yourself to be disturbed by petty annoyances. Always have a positive attitude towards everything, especially the more difficult problems you encounter. Let your thoughts always be positive:

'Whatever is true, whatever is honourable, whatever is just, whatever is pure, whatever is lovely, whatever is gracious, if there is any excellence, if there is anything worthy of praise, think about these things. What you have learned and received and heard and seen in me, do; and the God of peace will be with you.' (Philippians 4:8–9).

Know too that you communicate telepathically with others. By spiritual law, what you give out returns to you multiplied. Every thought you think in the present moment is creating your future. All destructive thoughts create stress and weaken the life force. Constantly use positive affirmations to impress positive beliefs on the subconscious mind and give thanks always that you have already received what you are looking for. (*The Game of Life and How to Play It* Scovel-Shinn.)

5. Always be truthful both to yourself and the other by being direct and calm with the other, especially in difficult situations. Never lose your calmness by losing your temper. By keeping your calmness, you retain your connectedness

with your higher self.

6. It is so important not to withdraw love from another if you are to remain healthy yourself. You must learn to forgive. Start by forgiving yourself. Your own personality needs the forgiveness of your own spirit. Forgive when you have been hurt by another and then let go. Unconditional love and forgiveness go hand in hand and that does not mean condoning the wrongdoing of another. What it does mean, however, is that you do not require that the other behave in any particular way in order to be loved. Unconditional love is learning to be the source of love rather than waiting for others to be the source. It is more important to have loving relationships than to hold on to the need to be right.

7. Do not stress yourself out so that you have no energy left at the end of the day. Do only what needs to be done today. Get plenty of rest, relaxation, exercise and fresh air and don't allow the pace of life to become so frenetic that your life force is constantly eroded.

8. Renew your connectedness with nature and with your creative side. When you do, you will become aware of the interdependence of every living creature and what nature has to teach you. Show respect for Mother Earth in all your practices as she is the one who nurtures you. Go for regular walks outdoors to rid your body of toxicity, to allow ground vitality or prana to enter your body through your feet and to appreciate the wonders of nature. Walking for twenty minutes out of doors every day, regardless of weather conditions, is absolutely necessary for the health of your bones. The natural light you receive in that time will energise you and provide you with the vitamin D so vital for the absorption of calcium from the intestine. Always breathe deeply. In doing so you will absorb air prana. Use your diaphragm to fill your lungs with fresh air and to get rid of toxins. This practice will help to calm your body and is particularly helpful to the gut. Gardening is a very therapeutic practice keeping you in the moment and energising you through contact with the earth. Try your hand at pottery, art or any other creative activity if you have an opportunity to do so.

9. Love yourself and others unconditionally. Be truthful and just to yourself and look for truth and justice for yourself from others. Never accept any situation where another is showing you anything less than respect. If this should happen, it is an opportunity for learning given to both parties. By being centred, you will have the awareness, the intuition and the courage to act. You are then giving the other the opportunity to learn to have respect for all. To become a doormat for others is to lack respect for yourself. Be careful, too, of falling into the trap of giving too much and not looking for anything in return. Always keep your cup

half full. When you do something for another let it always be because you want to, not because you have to. The latter causes resentment and consequent exhaustion.

In summary, you must become a detached witness to all the happenings in your own life knowing that in the physical world everything changes and all will pass. Becoming the detached witness means you are able to function at a healthier and more productive level. You become aware that every experience in your life, especially the most difficult, is of benefit to you and is for your growth and understanding. When you are able to live in the spiritual domain of witness, nothing goes wrong. Compassion replaces the need to control and to be right. You become more aware of, and make the most of opportunities to love yourself and others unconditionally. It is possible to experience heaven on earth when you are directed by the higher self rather than the ego. In one of the White Eagle publications called *The Quiet Mind*, we are given the following excellent blueprint for living: 'Say little, love much, give all, judge no man, aspire to all that is pure and good and keep on keeping on.' I believe that if we could live by that spiritual law, we would be healthier and happier for it.

The need for this book

Conventional wisdom states that the coeliac diet is a 'diet for life'. Most, if not all, patients accept this and resign themselves to this 'diet for life'. My belief is that the wheat-free, gluten-free diet is very important and very necessary for those who have been placed on it. The diet brings about almost immediate relief from pain and discomfort and allows the tissues to heal, but it does not bring about cure. While I am certainly not suggesting that you should ignore conventional wisdom—quite the contrary—I believe that this diet is only the first step in overcoming your health problems. You are body, mind and spirit. All need your attention if you are to have a strong and vibrant life force and consequently good health. My belief is that all illness is curable and that we ourselves have the greatest part to play in that cure. 'With God all things are possible'(Matt. 19: 26). If presented with the right conditions, the body has a marvellous ability to heal itself. You must take responsibility for, and work at, having good health. Don't give that responsibility away to anyone. Correct diet and exercise are the first steps in overcoming your health problems. Let awareness be the next step. In order to be aware, you must learn to live in the present moment. When you live consciously in the moment, you get in touch with the immeasurable power within you and you will become open to all possibilities. Learn about meditation and put it into practice in your life. Keep reading about the body, mind, spirit, approach to health and happiness and put it into practice in your life. In the meantime enjoy the recipes in the book!

I have researched and written this book with great love for you. My intention is to bring you great enjoyment, whether you are cooking for yourself alone or for family and friends. Be sure to make things as easy for yourself as possible by cooking the same for all. When you are preparing food, always be centred and prepare it with great love in your heart for all who will partake of it. In this way the food will be both spiritually and physically nourishing. Use organic ingredients where possible. The recipes in the book are designed to be nourishing, satisfying, and delicious. Most are just as good as their counterparts made with wheat, and some are even better. However, some recipe results may be a disappointment to you because your expectations are for something that only the properties of gluten can produce, for example crusty bread. This book should help to bring great variety into your diet and make eating, despite the diet, a great joy. Having this book will enable you to cook with confidence for anyone on a wheat-free, gluten-free diet.

Who could benefit from this book?

Those suffering from coeliac disease and those with an allergy to wheat will get almost immediate relief from symptoms when these recipes are followed. Other allergy sufferers, migraine sufferers, and those with bowel problems such as Crohn's disease, diverticulitis, colitis, irritable bowel and leaky gut may benefit from abstinence from wheat and/or gluten. Recent research has shown that autistic children may also benefit from a wheat- and gluten-free diet. Others who could also benefit are those suffering from arthritis and those with attention deficit disorder. The book should be helpful to people in the catering industry, enabling them to adapt most recipes to fit the special dietary needs of the wheat and/or gluten allergic. Apart from being wheat-free and gluten-free, the recipes in this book are not restrictive in any way though you will find that some recipes also happen to be dairy-free by their nature. Though the book is aimed especially at those mentioned above, everyone the world over can benefit from it. Follow the holistic wisdom contained here and you will glimpse heaven on earth. Follow the recipes and you will eat with joy.

Foods to eat and foods to avoid

Gluten, a protein found in the grain family, is a difficult protein to digest and particularly so for those with a weakened life force. It is present in wheat, oats, barley, rye and spelt.

In coeliac disease the small intestine becomes so damaged by gluten that the villi (little projections from the wall of the intestine which are responsible for absorption of the digested food products) become flat and cannot absorb food properly. When the disease is very severe the entire small intestine is affected and consequently there is a loss of most nutrients which in a healthy intestine are absorbed with ease. Fat, protein, sugar, iron, calcium, folic acid, vitamin A, vitamin E, vitamin K and sometimes vitamin B12 are carried out of the body. Loss of weight and diarrhoea, abdominal swelling and discomfort may be a consequence of this malabsorption. Nowadays, with a wheat-free diet for babies and early diagnosis it is very rare for someone to suffer from such severe symptoms. Generally only part of the small intestine is affected. If the problem is only in the duodenum (the first loop of the small intestine) anaemia may result from a lack of iron and folic acid. If the problem has extended to the middle section of the small intestine symptoms related to the malabsorption of proteins, sugars, fats, the fat-soluble vitamins, calcium and other minerals may result.

In clinics today the most frequently seen symptoms of the coeliac condition are anaemia, osteoporosis and amenorrhoea (the absence or stopping of the menstrual period). Other symptoms that may appear are recurrent mouth ulcers, fatigue, and a skin disorder known as *dermatitis herpetiformis* (DH), which affects about 5 per cent of coeliac patients. With this skin condition parts of the body, especially the elbows, shoulders, buttocks, sacrum, scalp and face have groups of clear blisters that itch very badly. DH is developed only by those suffering from coeliac disease. Usually they have a less severe form of the disease with less change to the intestine than in those with coeliac disease only. DH sufferers should avoid foods high in iodine such as sea vegetables or iodised table salt, as iodine is known to make the condition worse. Those diagnosed as suffering from the coeliac condition (this group includes those with DH), must eliminate all the gluten-containing grains (wheat, oats, barley, rye and spelt) from their diet. When they are removed the intestine (and also the skin in the case of DH sufferers) returns to normal. It is important that the diet is adhered to in a very strict manner, as a small quantity of gluten is sufficient to prevent the re-growth of the villi or to cause them to disappear again where they had repaired themselves. (However, do read my introduction to this book on the body, mind, spirit approach to good health.) Wheat or other gluten-containing cereals should not be given to babies until they are at least a year old, as their immune and digestive systems are not fully developed.

What you can eat to replace wheat if you have coeliac disease

Those who have coeliac disease can replace wheat with rice, millet, maize, buckwheat, chestnuts, soya beans, chickpeas, sago, tapioca and potatoes. Derivatives of these can all be used including rice flour, rice flakes, ground rice, cornflour (maize flour), buckwheat flour, chestnut flour, soya bean flour, chickpea flour (gram flour), sago flour, tapioca flour, potato flour and blends of naturally gluten-free flours. Rice bran and soya bran can be used to add fibre to the diet. Linseeds are an excellent source of fibre and are also a rich source of essential fatty acids. Arrowroot powder can be used for thickening. In Europe, most doctors and coeliac societies consider starch from which most of the gluten has been removed to be acceptable in the coeliac diet. This wheat starch must be approved by the standards body, Codex Alimentarius and most of the commercial breads sold in this country for coeliacs are made with Codex Alimentarius quality wheat starch. Up to 200 parts per million of gluten are allowed in this starch. In the USA and Canada wheat starch is not considered safe for use by those with the coeliac condition. You should be aware of the possibility of contamination of grains: during the transport or in the milling or packaging stages of naturally gluten-free grains and their products there may be contamination, thus there is a permitted level of gluten of 50 parts per million in these products. Kitchen grain mills are available for milling your own flour or flakes. Using these to grind your own grains, pulses and nuts reduces the possibility of contamination.

Suitability of oats for coeliacs

Recent studies in Finland and Ireland have shown that a certain amount of oats (not more than 2 oz/50 g per day) can be tolerated by coeliacs without any ill effects. However, the oats must be pure. Oats sold for general consumption may not be pure as they can be contaminated with wheat either in the fields, in transport, in the mills or during packaging. The purity of oats needs to be certified. Doctor's advice should be sought before including pure oats in the diet.

Wheat allergy

Most wheat-allergic patients are intolerant of the wheat grain in its entirety. Some, but very few, may be allergic only to its gluten content. Other wheat-allergic people can tolerate oats, barley, rye and spelt despite their gluten content.

A whole range of symptoms, some quite different from the coeliac patient's, can be seen among the wheat-sensitive or allergic. Very little research has been done on the wheat-allergic patient and therefore little is known about the condition.

What you can eat to replace wheat if you suffer from wheat allergy

Wheat allergy sufferers can replace wheat in their diet with rice, millet, maize, buckwheat, chestnuts, soya beans, chickpeas, sago, tapioca and potatoes. Derivatives of these can all be used including rice flour, ground rice, cornflour (maize flour), buckwheat flour, chestnut flour, soya bean flour, chickpea flour (gram flour), sago flour, tapioca flour and potato flour. Rice bran, soya bran and linseeds can all be used as can arrowroot. Blended flours derived from naturally wheat- and gluten-free grains can also be used. In addition to these foods, wheat allergy sufferers may be able to tolerate oats, barley, rye, and spelt. However, as these grains contain gluten they are not suitable for those suffering from the coeliac condition. Commercial products with these four grains can often contain wheat so vigilance is necessary. Wheat starch (wheat flour from which the gluten has been removed) and products made from wheat starch, would not be suitable for most wheat allergy sufferers. *All the recipes in this book are suitable for both the coeliac condition and wheat allergy.*

Breadmaking for coeliacs and the wheat-allergic

Bread baking poses a particular difficulty for those who have to exclude gluten or wheat from the diet. It is the marvellously stretchy and binding qualities of gluten that make wheat so wonderful for baking, producing light crusty rolls and bread. With naturally gluten-free flours, baking is more difficult but not impossible and some things can taste even better! A number of different brands of naturally wheat-/gluten-free flour blends, bread mixes, prepared breads and pizza bases are now available to suit both the coeliac and the wheat-allergic but I prefer to use the naturally wheat- and gluten-free flours that have no additives. Commercially prepared flour mixes and bread mixes often contain either guar gum or xanthan gum. These are added to help with the rising process. Wheat-/

gluten-free baking powder and yeast are available—believe it or not some yeast contains wheat so check with the shop or manufacturer before buying. I use soaked or ground linseeds as a natural binder in many of my recipes.

Buying processed foods

In addition to the foods already mentioned, which are naturally wheat- and gluten-free, the following foods in their natural state are all wheat- and gluten-free: meat, fish, poultry, eggs, fruit, vegetables, nuts, natural cheese, milk, cream, oil, sugar, honey, coffee, tea, pure spices. However, when processed in any way, these foods may contain wheat and/or gluten. Wheat and wheat derivatives can turn up in the most unexpected places. Who would expect to find wheat as a thickener in yogurt? It can happen. In fact wheat and/or gluten can turn up under many different guises. Here are some of the unsafe ingredients to look out for in packaging labels: modified starch, edible starch, thickeners, fillers, binders, mustard powder, dry roasted nuts, drinking chocolate, malt, malt flavouring, malt extract, hydrolysed vegetable protein, vegetable protein, cereal, cereal protein, monosodium glutamate, couscous, semolina, bulgar, wheat germ, pearl barley etc. Barley enzymes are often used in the processing of rice and soya beverages. Even sweeteners and stabilisers can be made from chemically modified wheat flour. The list is endless! Thus the importance of reading every label. Do not take a chance. Contacting the manufacturer can be very informative and has the added benefit of raising awareness about the problems of wheat and gluten intolerance.

Eating out

Wheat flour is extensively used in soups, terrines, gravy, sauces, white pepper, coatings, batters, stuffing, stews, even in mashed potato. Food which is wheat-/gluten-free to begin with can become contaminated by frying in oil in which other foods containing wheat were previously cooked. Freshly-made potato chips for example, may become contaminated by being fried in oil in which sausages containing wheat were previously fried. Eating out becomes even more difficult in restaurants that buy in processed foods. Frozen chips may be manufactured from extruded potato and contain wheat or may have a coating containing wheat. Dining-out cards available from coeliac societies are a great asset to members. A caring chef will be only too delighted to listen to your dietary needs but it is important to speak directly to the chef rather than to the waiting staff. If in doubt do not take a chance. You are not being a nuisance, you are a teacher helping to make the world a more caring place for those with special needs!

Gluten-free symbol

Many people will be familiar with the logo for gluten-free foods i.e. the wheat head with the line through it. This is not an indication that the food is wheat-free and should not be relied upon by those who are either wheat allergic or coeliac. Always check the labels. Those who suffer from the coeliac condition should look for the words 'gluten-free'. If in doubt check with the manufacturer, with the nutritionists employed by the large supermarket chains or with the very helpful assistants in the many health food shops around the country. Vigilance is necessary as manufacturers may change the ingredients in a product at any stage without regard for those with allergies. Always read the labels to be safe.

All the recipes in this book are both gluten-free and wheat-free. As far as possible I have used permitted ingredients in their most natural state. Apart from the obvious nutritional benefits, this avoids the need to read labels. Where you need to use any commercially prepared ingredients in the recipes make sure to check the labels to ensure the product is wheat- and/or gluten-free.

Some plant foods to nourish you

As I researched this book, I was reminded of my father's story about Mrs Delaney's Chocolate Mould. Mrs Delaney was a neighbour of my grandmother, Ma. One day she told Ma that she had made a wonderful chocolate mould. 'Now,' she said, 'the recipe says cornflour but I don't have that so I use flour. I don't have milk so I use water. I cannot afford chocolate so I use cocoa. It tells me to sweeten with caster sugar, but I use ordinary sugar and I don't have a mould so I use a basin!' Now if Mrs Delaney could make a chocolate mould without any of the ingredients surely you and I are not going to be fazed because we can't include wheat and gluten! As they say in Cork, Mrs Delaney would have had a gala with all the products that she could have used instead of wheat and so will you!

Rice and rice products

Rice grains Whole grain or brown rice contains all the nutrients of the grain including those contained in the outer layers. Despite this, most rice used today is of the polished kind, that is, white rice. When rice is polished by pounding, the outer layer of bran is removed. The polishing also destroys a large portion of the B vitamins and the minerals present in the grain. Although polished rice has been shown to have more proteins available to the body, brown rice is preferable because it has more fibre, minerals and B vitamins. All rice is a wonderful source of complex carbohydrate in the form of starch and rice is particularly good in the diets of diabetics. Brown rice does not keep as long as white. Like all wholegrain products, it tends to go rancid over time. It should be kept in the refrigerator and used by the 'best before' date. If brown rice is soaked before cooking, the soaking liquid should be used for boiling the rice to prevent the loss of the B vitamins (see page* on the cooking of rice). Some manufacturers parboil the rice and this has the effect of driving the water-soluble B vitamins into the centre of the grain. If rice is not par-boiled more of the B vitamins are lost. Brown rice, together with fruit and vegetables, has a very cleansing effect on the body.

Many different grades and varieties of rice are now available. The expensive *Basmati rice* comes from the Himalayas and is very delicately flavoured. In India and Kashmir it is reserved for special occasions. *Thai jasmine rice* is similar in flavour and is sometimes described as scented, fragrant or perfumed rice because it smells so good in the cooking. It is slightly sticky when cooked. The stickiest of all rice when cooked is *glutinous rice*. No! It does not contain gluten! It is given this name because it is so sticky. *Arborio rice* is a short grained rice and is one of the varieties used in risotto as it has an ability to absorb lots of liquid and has a creamy consistency. *Camargue rice* is a short grain rice which is red in colour and is very attractive in salads. *Wild rice* is not rice at all but the seed of an aquatic grass. It was at one time the principal food of the Native Americans.

Rice noodles are made from rice. They come in both the traditional noodle shape and also in a flat ribbon-like form and are commonly used in Thai, Vietnamese, Singaporean and Chinese dishes. They are really convenient as they require very little cooking. Place them in a bowl, cover them with boiling water, put a lid on top and leave undisturbed for 15 minutes. Then drain and use them according to the recipe. However, rice noodles are a very processed product and for that reason should only be used occasionally.

I use a lot of *brown rice flour* in baking cakes, bread and scones. The brand called Doves Farm is very satisfactory and is labelled gluten-free. As this flour does not contain gluten, it will not behave in the same way as wheat flour. In recipes where air can be incorporated in the mixture, as in sponge cake and victoria sponge cake, a very good result, hardly distinguishable from that of similar cakes made with wheat flour, can be achieved. Rice flour is quite grainy so the texture of the finished cake is slightly sandy, but the taste is yummy! There is one great benefit to using rice flour—it is quite sweet, so you need less sugar than usual.

Brown rice flakes Rice flakes milled from brown rice can be used for porridge and for puddings. The flakes are easy and quick to use and have all the benefits of brown rice. It is a very convenient and nutritious food for young children and ideal as a breakfast cereal.

Rice powder, also called white rice flour Rice powder is a very finely ground flour made from white rice, available from Asian stores. Anywhere I have used brown rice flour, white rice powder could be used instead but brown rice flour is, of course, the healthier option. If you want to make a very smooth and glossy white or béchamel sauce, rice powder makes an ideal substitute for wheat flour. It has greater thickening power than wheat flour so less is required.

Ground rice is coarser than rice flour. It can be used for puddings, crumbles and for coating burgers, fish cakes, and the like.

Rice bran is the outside layer of the rice kernel. Rich in dietary fibre it contains many of the nutrients not found in white rice. A popular brand is Ener-G.

Rice cakes are not made from polystyrene beads as many have suggested! The rice is heated for a few seconds at 270°C which makes it puff up. It is then pressed into shape to form rice cakes.

Puffed rice cereal in its purest form is both wheat- and gluten-free. Some of the more well-known brands, however, use malt as a flavouring which renders them unsuitable for those with coeliac disease. The brand KALLO is both wheat- and gluten-free and is made from organic whole grain rice.

Potatoes

The potato was brought to Europe from Peru. Potatoes, like wheat and rice, are a very important source of starch in the diet. They also contain all the essential amino acids, calcium, iron, niacin (vitamin B3), thiamine (vitamin B1), folic acid, vitamin C and dietary fibre. Second only to green leafy vegetables in providing us with folic acid potatoes are not fattening in themselves but become so if eaten as crisps or chips or with loads of added butter. The vitamins and minerals are stored just beneath the skin and for that reason potatoes are best cooked in their jackets. Potatoes which have been sunburned and are green should be avoided.

Potato flour can be used for thickening and in baking. It is a very processed product and is almost pure starch.

Linseeds

Linseeds, also called flaxseeds, are a wonderful source of a soluble, mucilaginous type of dietary fibre. This type of fibre is very gentle on the digestive tract compared to bran. Linseeds are also rich in the essential fatty acids, particularly linolenic acid. They can be added to cereal, breads, scones, pancakes, soups, stews etc. It is important to drink plenty of water with linseeds. Do not exceed 6–8 tablespoons per day and grind them to obtain the maximum benefit.

Maize and maize products

Maize grain We commonly know maize grain as corn-on-the-cob or sweetcorn. It is not a very nutritious grain as it is not only deficient in lysine but also in another essential amino acid called tryptophan and in the B vitamin niacin. Much of the maize now grown is genetically modified (GM). This technology is already known to be damaging to the environment. It has not yet been proved to be safe to human health and there is a lot of consumer resistance to GM foods. This is sufficient reason to buy organic maize and its products. Many manufacturers of wheat-/gluten-free products are avoiding the use of GM ingredients.

Cornflakes are made from maize and are sometimes heavily fortified with vitamins. They often contain added gluten under the guise of malt. Organic wheat-

/gluten-free cornflake products from several different companies are available.

Maize flour, cornflour and polenta are all made from corn-on-the-cob. Maize flour is creamy-yellow in colour. The finest flour is called cornflour and is almost pure starch. Maize flour and cornflour are used in baking and for thickening. A slightly more coarsely ground maize flour is known as medium maize meal while the most coarsely ground is called coarse maize meal or polenta. There is also an instant version of polenta available which cooks in a fraction of the time it takes for traditional polenta.

Chickpea (or gram) flour is milled from garbanzo beans or chickpeas. They are beige in colour and make a strong-tasting yellow flour which can be used in small quantities in baking cakes, bread and pancakes. As peas, they can be eaten (like all pulses) with wholegrain cereals to provide the body with complete proteins.

Mexican tortillas Maize may be made into flat bread such as corn tortillas. In preparing Mexican corn tortillas the grains are heated in limewater and then made directly into dough and cooked on a hot iron plate. The use of limewater makes the vitamin niacin in the maize available to the body. Flour tortillas are made from wheat flour and are not the same as Mexican corn tortillas. It is important to read the label on the packs when buying tortillas.

Soya products

There are many soya products on the market today including soya beans, soya flour, soya bran, soy sauce, miso, tofu, soya milk, soya oil, textured vegetable protein (TVP) etc. Some contain wheat so do be vigilant about reading labels. Soya products are rich in phytoestrogens and can be very helpful to menopausal women. Unfortunately, much of the world's soya is now genetically modified and this, together with the fact that it is not segregated at source from traditional soya, means that it is more difficult to obtain the pure traditional kind. Allergies have risen dramatically and coincidentally since the introduction of GM soya into the food chain and because of this it is best to avoid it if you are not absolutely sure that it is either traditional or organic.

Soya beans, like other beans, peas and lentils, are legumes. Soya beans are a particularly valuable source of protein as they contain all the essential amino acids. Like all pulses they are rich in dietary fibre. They are also rich in linoleic acid which is one of the essential fatty acids. Soya beans also contain calcium, iron, some B vitamins, vitamin E and lecithin.

Soya flour Milled from soya beans, soya flour is very nutritious adding an attractive nutty flavour to baked goods. Ideally, it should be stored in the fridge. *Soya bran* has a very musty taste, so tastewise it is not the best. However, it is a good source of fibre and effective in the treatment and prevention of constipation.

Soy sauce is widely used in Chinese and Japanese cookery. It is made from fermented soya beans and wheat. Look for tamari soy sauce made entirely from fermented soya beans but do check the label!

Miso is a brown paste made from fermented soya bean. It is available either pasteurised or unpasteurised; the unpasteurised type is preferable. There are three varieties—barley miso, wheat miso and brown rice miso. For those who are wheat and/or gluten allergic the only permitted one is brown rice miso. In the manufacturing process, the grain and beans are digested by enzymes and this makes miso very nutritious and easily digestible. As miso contains all the essential amino acids, it is a complete protein and, in addition, contains Vitamin B12, which is quite difficult for anyone who is a vegetarian or vegan to include in sufficient quantity in the diet. Miso discharges toxins from the body and has an ability to discharge even radioactive elements. The Japanese use the unpasteurised kind to restore and maintain a normal bowel flora as it contains lactobacillus. If you have been on antibiotics and wish to restore your bowel flora or if you want to maintain a good bowel flora, have ¼ teaspoon of unpasteurised brown rice miso, also called genmai miso, every day. Miso, which is very salty, can be made into instant soup by adding hot but not boiling water to it. Blanched julienne of vegetables can be added to the soup before eating.

Tofu is soya bean cheese. It is very high in protein and low in calories. In the Western world it is eaten mainly by vegans, vegetarians and those allergic to dairy products. Look for organic tofu made from nigari. Tofu can be used for sauces, soups and as a filling in sandwiches, and can be marinated, stirfried, boiled or steamed.

Millet and millet products

Millet grain Three major types of millet are produced in the world and these are sorghum, finger millet and bull-rush millet. The latter is the familiar pearl millet available in health food shops. A hardy millet grown in the cold regions of South America is known as quinoa. Millet is a very nutritious gluten-free grain, rich in the amino acid methionine. It combines very well with beans in a vegan diet to ensure a full complement of amino acids which are the building blocks for proteins. It is a wonderful grain to substitute for wheat gluten as its protein quality is higher. Millet grain cooks like rice and can be substituted for rice in most dishes.

Millet flake It is best to buy millet flake in a shop which has a good turnover of stock as it can go rancid. It is very useful and nutritious as a breakfast cereal, either cooked as porridge or used as a base for a gluten-free museli. It can be used for crumble toppings where it produces a particularly appealing crunchy result. It is also good in breads and can replace breadcrumbs in plum pudding and in crumb coatings.

Buckwheat and buckwheat products

Buckwheat is not a grain, but is rather the fruits of the plant which is related to the dock leaf family. It thrives in poor soil and in cool, moist climates and is seen as the ideal food in those areas as it has a warming and drying effect on the body. Buckwheat has a strange flavour but is rich in B vitamins and in the essential amino acid lycine. It is popular as a wintertime dish in Eastern European countries where it is it is often roasted before being cooked like rice. *Buckwheat noodles* Buckwheat is also popular in Japan where they eat it as Soba noodles. Beware! most Soba noodles contain a certain amount of wheat.

Buckwheat flour has a strong flavour and is used mainly in making pancakes and batters. It is also an ingredient in Doves Farm gluten-free, wheat-free, flour blend which I have used in some of my recipes.

Buckwheat flakes can be cooked like porridge and served for breakfast.

Pasta

Although those on a wheat-/gluten-free diet cannot have wheat pasta, they can have pasta dishes made from corn pasta or rice pasta or pasta made from combinations of corn, rice and millet. Look out for the naturally coloured rice pastas as they can be particularly attractive. Special pastas are relatively expensive compared to their wheat counterparts. Pasta dishes can also be made using wheat-/gluten-free pancakes instead of dried pasta.

Tapioca

Tapioca is made from the tubers of the cassava shrub and is almost pure starch. It is gluten free. Tapioca flour can be purchased from Asian food stores and you will find that it is an ingredient in some special breads.

Sago

Sago is derived from the pith of the Sago palm. The tree is felled and split and the starch washed out. It, too, is almost devoid of protein and is almost all starch. Though tapioca and sago puddings were at one time very popular, today they would appear to be out of fashion!

Arrowroot

Arrowroot is another source of starch which is gluten free and used for thickening.

Wheat-/gluten-free baking powder and yeast

Wheat-/gluten-free baking powder is generally based on potato flour and quite a few brands are available. Fresh yeast is difficult to source. I have used instant dried yeast where yeast is required. Check that the yeast you buy is wheat- and gluten-free.

Sprouted seeds

The seeds of plants have a concentrated food supply in order to feed the tiny plant embryo until it develops roots and shoots. A seed, whether a pulse, a nut or a cereal seed, contains proteins, carbohydrates, fats, vitamins and minerals. When the seed absorbs moisture, the enzymes in the seed become active and lots of chemical changes take place inside the seed. These chemical changes convert the proteins to amino acids and the starch to glucose. The vitamin content increases and the minerals are very easy for the human body to use. Sprouted seeds are therefore of very high nutritional value. And even better news—most of the gas-producing starches in beans are eliminated as a result of sprouting! (For vegans the sprouts of legumes and the use of miso are almost the only ways of getting vitamin B12 naturally in the diet).

The *seeds most suitable for sprouting are*: adzuki beans, mung beans, peas, chickpeas, lentils, alfalfa, sunflower seeds, mustard seeds and cress seeds. The pulse sprouts available commercially are generally mung beans, alfalfa and lentils.

To sprout your own seeds, firstly soak about 2 tablespoons of the seeds overnight. (This is not necessary for alfalfa and cress seeds as they are so small.) Drain and rinse them in clean water and transfer them to a sprouting tray or a large glass jar (a large coffee jar or Kilner jar would be suitable). Place a muslin lid on top and secure it with an elastic band. Turn the jar upside down to drain for a little while then place it on its side in a warm place out of direct sunlight. The temperature should be around 20°C to start germination. Rinse the seeds twice a day and drain them. Sprouts should be ready for eating in 3–6 days depending on the seed size and type.

To use the sprouted seeds rinse them thoroughly and blanch them (do not blanch alfalfa, mustard or cress, as they are so delicate) as follows: plunge the sprouts into boiling water. Bring the water back to the boil and boil for about one minute, then drain the sprouts and plunge them into cold water. Drain them again and when you are sure that they have been cooled completely by the cold water transfer them to the fridge for storage until required. They will keep for a few days in a sealed container. Sprouted seeds can be sprinkled on salads or used in stir-fries.

Dry roasted seeds and nuts

Though oil is best taken in its most natural state in the form of raw seeds and nuts, dry roasted seeds and nuts are really good in salads, adding crunch and nutritional value. Try roasting the following: sunflower seeds, sesame seeds, pumpkin seeds, almonds, cashews, pecans and pine nuts. Most seeds contain about two or three times as much fat as protein but nuts contain from three to seven times as much. Almonds are rich in calcium.

Do not buy preroasted seeds or nuts as they can be rancid and in addition often have coatings which may contain wheat and/or monosodium glutamate and lots of added salt.

To roast nuts or seeds, take a dry, heavy-based saucepan and place some nuts or seeds (one kind only at a time) into it, sufficient only to cover the bottom of the saucepan. Place the saucepan over gentle heat and roast the seeds slowly, stirring them all the time so that they don't burn. When they are nicely roasted, to a golden brown colour, turn them out onto a plate to stop the cooking. Sesame seeds will literally hop out of the saucepan when they start to roast or if the temperature is too high. Once they start to hop, turn the heat down and stir until roasted. It is a good idea to pound the roasted sesame seeds with a pestle and mortar to facilitate digestion.

Pulses

Pulses are nutritionally very desirable. Peas, beans and lentils, though deficient in the amino acid methionine, have plenty of lysine—the amino acid which is limited in cereals. Together, pulses and grains complement each other completely to give an ideal balance of essential amino acids. This is an important point for vegetarians and even more important for vegans who do not include dairy products or eggs in their diet. Pulses are also very high in fibre and B vitamins. They lower blood fats and decrease hardening of the arteries. Less fat and more fibre are very important in producing clean coronary arteries. One study showed that, in all races and all socio-economic groups, those who had a high consumption of vegetable proteins, i.e. beans, peas and lentils, had the cleanest arteries of all. Many people avoid pulses because they are notorious for causing flatulence or intestinal gas. If you would like to start including them in your diet, eat only very small amounts at first.

The traditional cuisine of India and China legumes (peas, beans, and lentils) are eaten in small amounts, perhaps only as much as one cupful of a vegetarian dish containing legumes a day, divided between two meals. Legumes would always be served with at least twice the quantity of cooked rice, bread or other kind of grain dish. We can learn from the example of Eastern peoples to eat legumes often, but only in small quantities.

Cooking dried pulses Dried pulses should be rinsed under the cold tap before soaking in cold water. Six to eight hours soaking time is necessary for most pulses but split red lentils do not need soaking and it is optional for black-eyed beans, split peas, green lentils and mung beans. After soaking, the pulses must be drained, rinsed again and covered with fresh water for boiling. Do not use salt in the water while boiling the pulses as this makes the skins tough. However, you can use herbs, onion, spices, bay leaves etc. in the water to add flavour. Pulses can take anything from 30 minutes to three hours to cook depending on the variety. They are ready when they are soft. Generally, soya beans take the longest time and red lentils the shortest with most other varieties taking about 1–1 ½ hours boiling time. Red kidney beans and black beans contain a toxin which can cause vomiting and diarrhoea if the beans are not cooked thoroughly.

The gas reducing method If you would like to take beans in your diet but find that they are causing you to lose friends, try the following! Take the soaked beans, drain them, and boil them in clean water for five minutes. Drain them again and soak them again in cold water for 20 minutes. Then rub the hulls off until they float free. Then boil again until they are thoroughly cooked. This should remove 85 per cent of the offending starches. A lot of work, but worth it to save embarrassment!

Juices

Juices that are home-made and drunk immediately are packed with vitamins and minerals. Ideally, juices should be made from organic ingredients. If you are in the need of a vitamin and mineral boost and you have a juicer, try juicing the following organic fruits and vegetables: apples, pears, celery, carrots, beetroot, cabbage etc. Try cocktails of these fruits and vegetables to make delicious drinks. Boil the mixtures and thicken them with the juice from a small organic potato to produce instant organic soups! Have one glass of juice a day. Vitamins that occur naturally in our food are much more readily available to the body than the commercially prepared kind.

Quick tips on choosing a balanced diet

✓ *Eat a wide variety* of the freshest, most wholesome, food (organic where possible).

✓ *Eat lots of complex carbohydrates* which can be found in potatoes and wholegrains e.g. brown rice, millet, buckwheat.

✓ *Eat lots of fruit and/or vegetables* with every meal. It is particularly important for coeliacs to include green leafy vegetables as they are high in iron, calcium and folic acid. Eat fruit—and vegetables too—as snacks between meals. As a basic rule of thumb, include fruit and/or vegetables in every meal. If the meal is something as simple as a boiled egg, start with a tossed salad or have an apple or fruit salad to finish.

✓ *Combine pulses (peas, beans and lentils) with wholegrains*, such as millet and brown rice, if you're vegan or vegetarian, to ensure proper amino acid balance. Tofu can also be used as its protein content is as good as meat or fish.

✓ *Use pulses, soya bran, rice bran and golden linseeds* to provide fibre in your diet.

✓ *Eat fresh fish, some chicken and red meat* for protein and iron, if you are not a vegetarian. The juice of a freshly squeezed orange taken at the same time will help to absorb the iron.

✓ *Include some dairy products and eggs.* Tinned sardines, which generally contain 550 mg of calcium per 100 g, are another excellent source of calcium. Molasses, broccoli and almonds also contain reasonably high values.

✓ *Use real butter* and *extra virgin cold pressed olive oil* sparingly. Summer butter is preferable to other butter as it is high in monounsaturates.

✓ *Avoid fatty foods.* Be aware of foods with hidden fats and avoid them.

✓ *Grill rather than fry.* A low temperature is best when frying. Avoid deep frying completely. The best way to get nutrient-rich oils in the diet is from fresh, raw seeds and nuts.

✓ *Go easy on salt* and salty foods as the sodium in salt tends to have an adverse effect on the utilisation of other minerals in the body and can cause high blood pressure if used in excess.

✓ *Drink at least four pints/2 litres* of water every day but if the supply is chlorinated, use bottled or filtered water instead. (Inline filters that remove the chlorine, the flourine (in fluoridated water) and any bacterial contamination from the water can be fitted to the cold water supply.)

✓ *Use coffee and tea sparingly* and weak. If you are partial to a few cups in the day, try to use real coffee and loose tea rather than instant or bags.

✓ *Cut down on cakes*, biscuits, sweets, and sugary drinks. Avoid drinks to which artificial sweeteners and flavourings have been added. Drink water with a slice of lemon instead.

✓ *Do not over-use convenience food* and when you must have it, make sure it's the best quality you can get.

✓ *Avoid GM foods* until they have been proved to be absolutely safe for both health and environment.

Substitutes for wheat and gluten

Here is a list of common ingredients, the foods they are found in and suggested wheat-/gluten-free substitutes. The recipes in this book give many examples of how to use them.

Flour made from wheat, rye, spelt, oats, barley found in *bread*
Wheat-/gluten-free bread made with the following flours (usually mixtures): brown rice flour, cornflour, maizeflour, polenta, potato flour, millet flake/flour, buckwheat flour, soya flour, gram flour.
Rice cakes, corn and rice crispbread, wheat-/gluten-free Mexican tortillas, wheat-/gluten-free pancakes and scones, potatoes, wheat-/gluten-free pasta and noodles, all kinds of rice, polenta.

Oats found in *porridge*
Brown rice, millet and buckwheat porridge.

Wheat flour found in *cakes*
Brown rice flour, cornflour, or mixtures of the two.

Wheat flour found in *sauces*
Brown rice flour, cornflour, white rice flour, potato flour.

Wheat found in *muesli*
Brown rice flakes, millet flakes, buckwheat flakes, wheat-/gluten-free muesli.

Wheat bran found in *cereals, muesli*
Rice bran, soya bran, linseeds.

Wheat found in *pizza base*
Wheat-/gluten-free pizza base.

Wheat, oats, malt found in *cereals*
Wheat-/gluten-free muesli, wheat-/gluten-free cornflakes, wheat-/gluten-free puffed rice cereal.

Wheat found in *pasta*
Wheat-/gluten-free pasta and noodles.

Wheat found in *milk puddings*
Rice, ground rice, sago, tapioca

Wheat found in *wheat flour coating on fish, burgers, rissoles, etc.*
Brown rice flour, cornflour, polenta, ground rice.

Wheat found in *breadcrumbs*
Millet flake, wheat-/gluten-free breadcrumbs.

Wheat found in *soy sauce*
Tamari soy sauce.

Wheat found in *miso*
Brown rice miso.

Wheat found in *sausages*
Wheat-/gluten-free sausages.

Wheat/gluten found in *stock cubes*
Wheat-/gluten-free stock cubes.

Wheat found in *baking powder*
Wheat-/gluten-free baking powder.

Food: shopping, storage, preparation

In the introduction I emphasised the importance of taking personal responsibility for one's own health. This responsibility extends to the sourcing, storage and cooking of food. It is especially important not to be complacent in this regard in the light of all the current food safety issues. Each one of us with spending power is in a position to bring about change in the way our food is produced. If we put a bit of thought into whom we buy from, where we buy, and what we buy, the resultant choices can make a huge difference to the quality of our lives and environment and the way in which food is produced.

Take your own shopping bags or boxes. This will help to reduce waste and pollution caused by plastic shopping bags. Try to support local businesses be they green grocers, health food stores, family butchers or Irish-owned supermarkets, local farmers' markets or the box scheme of the local organic farmer. (Three companies dominate the world's trade in fresh fruit, six the world's supply of grain!). There are good reasons for doing this. As these businesses will be more likely to source local produce than their multinational rivals, their produce will be fresh and have a strong life force and the money you spend will be kept in the local economy. Families will be supported, biodiversity (richness of varieties) protected, and air and noise pollution and road congestion caused by the transport of food reduced. The bigger multiples like to buy in bulk, want continuity of supply all year round and perfect looking packaged produce all the same size and shape. Varieties are often grown for long shelf life rather than taste or nutrition. These demands can only be met by large scale industrial agriculture through the intensive growing of plants and animals and the use of synthetic chemicals such as growth promoters, antibiotics and pesticides. Avoid as far as possible out of season and exotic fruit and vegetables. Out of season produce often means more chemicals and more packaging. Exotic fruits often come from developing countries which generally do not have very stringent controls on agro-chemicals. Countries producing out-of-season produce for us are often doing so to pay off unreasonable national debts. Consequently this land is unavailable for food crops for local people and their limited water supply is depleted. High nitrate levels will generally be present in green vegetables produced in winter in greenhouses. It is best to limit your intake of lettuce, spinach and cucumber produced in this way. Unseasonal produce also means that if our own growers cannot compete with overseas growers by supplying produce all year round, they may very well go out of business. Try to support the Fair Trade initiative which gives a better deal to Third World farmers and ensures control of agro-chemicals. Fair Trade products include tea, coffee and chocolate. Ask your retailer to stock them.

Buy Irish organic produce as far as possible. Sometimes it may not be perfect-looking but let go of the need for perfection. The cabbage with slug holes and plenty of 'livestock' between the leaves is far healthier than the one which is cosmetically perfect due to being sprayed with pesticide. Besides, it's good to see that the organic farmer grew enough for humans and non-humans alike! A recent report from Rutgers University shows that trace minerals were up to one hundred and seventy times greater in organic vegetables than in their conventionally produced equivalents. The macro-mineral (calcium, magnesium, potassium and sodium) content of the organic produce was between two and four times greater. An adequate intake of minerals is absolutely necessary for a healthy body.

Avoid convenience foods as they generally contain ingredients which are alien to the body, are totally devoid of any life force and usually contain high levels of sugar, salt, and fat.

Try to avoid plastic bottles and plastic wrapping on anything. Look for glass bottles and try to get cheese and other fat-containing foods wrapped in parchment rather than plastic. Plastics may contain endocrine-disrupting chemicals—most dangerous for the developing foetus and young children. If you have a choice between a loose item and a similar packed one, buy the loose.

When you are shopping for non-edible products such as cleaning agents and personal hygiene products cut down to a minimum the variety of products you buy and try to source those that will damage neither you nor the environment. Bring back into use such things as bread soda, vinegar, salt and washing soda which can be used instead and which are very cheap. Avoid unnecessary products such as air fresheners. Open the windows instead! Each one of us has a role to play in the health of our rivers, lakes, seas, soil and ground water. Think before you use any chemical. Where will it go when you release it into the environment? What will it do? Where will it end up? Perhaps in your food or water?

Produce of conventional farming

There are some things you should be aware of when you cannot get organic produce and have to make do (for the time being) with the produce of conventional farming. Generally speaking the 'quality' product on the supermarket shelf complies with the basic minimum standards or little more as laid down by the

Department of Agriculture and Food. (It is worth noting, however, that in this country our Environmental Protection Agency (EPA) licenses the farmland spreading of pharmaceutical and other industrial wastes and of treated human sewage sludge. Do you believe that these practices are in the interests of 'quality' food?)

Meat

The Quality Assurance scheme for pork and bacon still allows growth-promoting antibiotics. The meat does not require to be hung so it can be very tough. The breeding sows are tethered for up to ten months of the year despite the quality label.

It is difficult to know what to say about the purchase of beef at this time apart from recommending that you buy organic. However, a spokesperson for the Department of Agriculture and Food tells me that since 1996 there have been very stringent controls in place in this country to protect our cattle from BSE—controls that were far more stringent than most other European countries. It would appear that the big mistake made by our government was to continue to allow meat and bone meal to be used in this country for pigs and poultry which means that cattle feed could have been contaminated by the BSE prion either advertently or inadvertently. Buy beef from a reputable butcher or retailer, preferably one with a trace back scheme. Avoid convenience pies, burgers and other dishes containing beef.

Chicken

Much of the chicken eaten in this country is imported. The end product on the supermarket shelf may be 'Irish' but the chicken may have travelled from as far away as Thailand. This certainly adds to the food miles! In general the standards under which poultry are reared here are low. Much of our national flock is intensively reared causing distress to the birds. EU labels include 'free-range', which does not mean a whole lot; 'traditional free-range', which means something slightly better and 'free-range total freedom' which are the best quality free range but difficult to source.

The standard of chickens from some retailers, however, is slightly better nowadays than in recent times. These retailers insist on grain-fed chickens where the meals are free from GM ingredients, antibiotics and growth promoters. If your supplier cannot give you chicken produced to this standard, or cannot tell you anything about their production, go elsewhere.

Note: Meat and bone meal has been banned from all animal feed from 1 January 2001 for a six-month period. My belief is that consumers will require this ban to remain indefinitely.

Fish

Farmed salmon comes in three grades: 'Superior', 'Ordinary' and 'Production'. An earthy taste from the salmon indicates water pollution. Flabby muscle and wide streaks of fat on the salmon suggests that stocking density was too great in the fish farm. Look for fish produced in a farm located far off-shore where there is a good flow of water and where less pesticides and other chemicals will be necessary. Support the fishmonger who cares enough to know how and where the fish is farmed.

Cheese

Soft cheeses, whether pasteurised or not, should be avoided by pregnant women, those who are ill, the elderly and the very young as there is a slight chance of Listeria poisoning. The risk of Listeria is also associated with prepared salads, pates, chilled ready meals and cheese cakes.

Eggs

The best conventionally produced eggs you can hope to get are those with the IFREPA (Irish Free-Range Egg Producers Association) label or the Quality Assured label. These labels ensure that the eggs are from Salmonella controlled flocks and antibiotics are not allowed in the feed. Food containing raw or undercooked eggs should not be given to the elderly, the very young, the ill or pregnant women.

Fats and oils

When shopping for fats and oils, choose butter and extra virgin cold-pressed olive oil. Summer butter has the edge on other butter, as it is slightly higher in monounsaturates. The olive oil should be packed in dark glass bottles. Buy fresh seeds and nuts.

Avoid highly processed oils and the margarines and spreads made from them —the supermarkets stock a great variety. The oils are extracted using solvents and they are degummed (removing lots of nutrients), refined (treated with caustic soda), bleached and deodorized (removing the unpleasant tastes and odours that were not present in the natural oils to begin with). The resulting oils are nutrient-deficient and contain toxins. The margarines and spreads made from these oils are further processed, some of them undergoing hydrogenation. The latter process gives rise to more toxic substances.

Unrefined oils such as walnut and safflower oils will add variety to dressings but they are very difficult to obtain. The term 'cold pressed' used in connection with oils other than olive oil can be misleading. Apart from cold-pressed olive oil, it is almost impossible to find oils pressed without heat.

Fruit and vegetables

Conventionally produced fruit and vegetables can contain pesticide residues, have high nitrate levels, be coated in waxes and even be treated with post-harvest preservatives. Apples, pears and grapes are often heavily treated with pesticide and residues are often found in them. To reduce the pesticide content always peel anything that can be peeled. Always peel carrots and remove their tops. Washing is not very effective in removing pesticides as they are designed to cling. Some are systemic and get into the internal tissues of the plant. Waxes are often used to prevent fruits and vegetables from drying out. It is difficult to remove them even with hot soapy water. In citrus fruits the wax may contain preservatives. Post-harvest treatments may also be applied to many crops including apples, citrus fruits, grapes, wheat, potatoes, bananas, pears and cherries.

Ask your greengrocer about the produce she/he stocks. If we, the consumers, keep questioning we will create awareness and this is the first step in bringing about change.

Your actions, your thoughts and your words have a powerful effect on our world. Let your thoughts and words mirror the reality you want to create. Let your actions be lifegiving through the choices you make. By limiting or eliminating the toxic products you use, you are making a very real and valuable contribution to the health of all things. By supporting the organic industry you are making a statement about the way you want your food produced, your health protected and your environment cared for. As a result of each consumer's demand for organic produce, governments will have to put greater funding into organic research. Industrial agriculture and the stranglehold of the agrochemical industry will decline, the politics of food will change and food—though it may cost a little more—will be produced in a way that is health giving not only to humans but to the entire biotic community.

Shopping for food

Whether or not we eat organically we still need to be very vigilant about hygiene while shopping and in our food preparation to ensure that what we eat is safe. Remember that bacteria need three very basic things in order to multiply: food, moisture and a suitable temperature (5°C–63°C). Bacteria double in numbers every 10 to 20 minutes if they are provided with these conditions.

When shopping for fresh food, check the temperatures in the refrigerated display cabinets. Fridges should be at 4°C or lower while freezers should be at -18°C.

Don't buy food from display counters where raw and cooked foods are not separated or where assistants handle cooked food after handling raw meat or poultry without washing their hands.

Don't be taken in by the impression of hygiene often given by the wearing of plastic gloves. A person wearing plastic gloves must obey all the other hygiene rules.

Don't buy prepared salads from a self-service salad bar. The food may be chilled but there is nothing to stop anyone sneezing, coughing or handling the food. Spoon handles which have been handled by all users often end up in the food.

Don't buy cracked eggs.

Don't buy containers of fresh food if they have been left out of the fridge, for example, yogurt.

Don't buy swollen chilled food packages or cans, or leaking cans, bottles or containers or containers with imperfect seals.

Don't buy vacuum packed products where the pack is not tightly sealed around the product, e.g. rashers.

Don't buy mouldy or discoloured products. Aphlotoxins in moulds can cause food poisoning.

Don't buy cooked chickens or other hot counter products if they are only warm: they should be very hot.

Do use a cool box to transport frozen or chilled products if you have to travel a distance.

Preparing and storing food

Wash your hands with non-perfumed soap and water before you start to prepare food, regularly during its preparation and when you have finished.

Cover any cut on your hands with a clean waterproof bandage.

Do not cough or sneeze on food.

Wash fruit and vegetables thoroughly, and peel them where possible. This has become very necessary not only to reduce as far as possible any dirt or chemicals but to safeguard against E.coli 0157, a new and very nasty bacterium which can cause food poisoning when present in only very small numbers.

Cook food thoroughly to kill any bacteria that may be in the food. Due to the intensive nature of modern agriculture, there is a potential for poisoning bacteria such as Salmonella, Campylobacter or E. coli 0157 to be present more frequently than ever. Some of these may even be resistant to antibiotics. Therefore it is especially important to cook chicken, pork and processed meats such as burgers and sausages right through. The juices should run clear. If the juices are pink the food is not done.

Use designated chopping boards for raw and cooked meat, fruit and vegetables.

Keep chopping boards, kitchen utensils and surfaces meticulously clean.

Change kitchen cloths such as tea towels and dish cloths every day and wash the used ones separately from other clothes at the highest temperature in your washing machine.

Follow the manufacturer's instructions when reheating convenience food.

Protect food from flies and other pests.

Keep perishable foods in the fridge at or below 4°C.

In the fridge keep raw meat and poultry below cooked food to prevent them dripping onto or touching the cooked food.

Cover and store left-over cooked food in the fridge once the steam has evaporated from it.

Follow the 'use by' dates.

Use suitable containers for freezing food to prevent contamination and freezer burn.

Ideally defrost frozen food overnight, on a plate in the fridge.

If using a microwave to defrost, cook the food immediately afterwards as some parts of it may have become warm.

Use a Pyrex or porcelain container and avoid plastic wrap when heating or cooking food in the microwave. This will ensure that the food does not become contaminated with hormone-disrupting chemicals. This is especially important for pregnant women and young children.

Cook defrosted food immediately to over 70°C in order to kill bacteria and make the food safe.

Do not refreeze food that has been defrosted unless it has been cooked to over 70°C first.

Keep hot food very hot and cold food very cold. The danger zone for food is between 5°C and 63°C.

Useful utensils

The following utensils are available from most good department stores

♦ knives—good knives are absolutely essential in any kitchen. The best are available from suppliers to the catering industry. I would recommend a plastic handled office knife—short-handled, short-bladed—and tomato knife, a timber-handled chef's knife with a blade of about 8 inches/20 cm and a kitchen scissors. If the knives are treated with care they should last a lifetime.

♦ baking tray (non-stick)

♦ balloonwhisk

♦ bun tins

♦ chopping boards (wood is best for protecting your knives)

♦ Christmas cake tin 7 in/18 cm square or 8 in/20 cm diameter round

♦ electronic weighing scales

♦ food mixer

♦ food processor with grater attachment

♦ frying pans, non-stick: small 7 inch/18 cm and large 11½ inch/29 cm

♦ hand grater

♦ heavy-based casserole 6 pint/3 litre capacity

♦ juicer

♦ lemon squeezer

♦ liquidiser (the goblet kind for grinding linseeds and the in-pot kind for soups)

♦ loaf tin 8½ in x 4½ in/22 cm x 11.5 cm

♦ metal skewers (flat)

♦ ovenproof dish 2–3 pint/1–1½ litre capacity or slightly larger

- pepper mill
- pizza plate 10 in/25.5 cm diameter
- potato masher
- potato peeler (swivel peeler is easiest to use)
- roasting tin, large
- sandwich tin 6½ inch (16.5 cm) diameter (avoid aluminium)
- sieve (nylon) or stainless steel
- steamer, s tainless steel or in-pot butterfly steamer
- Swiss roll tin 8½ inch x 12½ inch/22 cm x 32 cm
- wooden spoons and lifters

Grain mills are available from
Munster Wholefoods
Farranfore
Co Kerry
Tel: 066-976-4691 Fax: 066-976-4692 Email: sales@mwf.ie
Web: www.mwf.ie

Inline water filters are available from
Simply Water, 62 Brighton Square, Dublin 6.

Knives are available by mail order from
Broderick Bros Ltd, J.F. Kennedy Industrial Estate, Dublin 12.

The recipes

♦   All the recipes in this book are both wheat- and gluten-free.

♦   All are suitable for both the coeliac condition and wheat allergy.

♦   Dairy-free recipes are indicated in the index as follows: ✓.

♦   The recipes were tested using Imperial measures, and converted into metric and North American measures subsequently.

♦   North American units of measure for dry ingredients are the same as for Imperial i.e. pounds, ounces.

♦   The North American unit for fluid ingredients is the cup measure.

         1 cup = 8 fluid ounces (Imperial)

         1¼ cups = ½ pint or 10 fluid ounces (Imperial)

♦   Butter is measured in both sticks and cups for your convenience.

         Abbreviations

         1 tsp = 1 teaspoon

         1 dstsp = 1 dessertspoon (= 2 tsps)

         1 tblsp = 1 tablespoon (= 2 dessertspoons)

'Today is a wonderful day,
I choose to make it so.'

Louise L. Hay

Breakfast

Even without special bread, breakfast is not a problem, as you will discover from the recipes in this chapter. Some of them are also ideal as snacks for any time of day.

I include some recipes for different kinds of pancakes—all are very versatile. Mix and match them with any of the suggested fillings or any of your own fillings. Pancakes can be made in advance and stored in the refrigerator separated by sheets of greaseproof or parchment paper and placed in a plastic bag. In the refrigerator they will keep for two or three days. To keep pancakes hot or to reheat them, place them on a plate, cover them, and place the plate over a pot of simmering water until heated through.

Rice, millet or buckwheat porridge

If you like a rich porridge you could use more milk than water in the proportions suggested. Use millet flakes from a supplier with a good turnover. Buckwheat has a distinctive taste which may not be to everyone's liking.

Serves 1

1/3 cup brown rice flakes or millet flakes or buckwheat flakes

1 cup of water or milk or ½ cup water and ½ cup milk

Put all the ingredients into a saucepan and cover. Allow to soak for 20 minutes or overnight.

Bring to the boil while stirring. Cook for about 3 minutes.

Serve the porridge on its own or with milk and/or sugar, honey or maple syrup.

Variations

Serve with stewed prunes, apricots, plums or berries.

Add washed dried fruits and 1 teaspoon ground linseeds to the rice flakes and soak.

Add 1 teaspoon of any nut butter of your choice just before serving and mix well.

Rice and banana breakfast

Serves 1

½ cup brown rice

1 tsp cashew nut butter or any nut butter of your choice

1 banana or other fruit of your choice, peeled and chopped

a drizzle of honey or maple syrup (optional)

1 dstsp rice bran (optional)

Cook the brown rice. When it is cooked stir in the nut butter. Add the chopped fruit, drizzle with the honey or syrup if using, and sprinkle with rice bran.

Rice and millet flake muesli

This is delicious muesli. Rice bran can be added if you like to increase the fibre. You could also add some seeds, nuts and/or puffed rice cereal.

dried fruit of your choice, as much or
    as little as you like
equal quantities brown rice flakes and
    millet flakes
honey to taste

rice bran, sesame seeds, sunflower
    seeds, nuts and/or puffed rice
    cereal (optional)

Wash the fruit. Dry it in a clean tea towel. Spread it out on a baking tray and finish drying it in a very slow oven. This will take 10–15 minutes. Remove the fruit from the oven.

Turn the heat up to 180°C/350°F/Gas 4. Mix the flakes (and bran, seeds and nuts if using). Spread the mixture onto a baking sheet, place in the oven and toast lightly until golden.

Remove from the oven. Drizzle some honey over the mixture. Add the dried fruit. When cold, add the puffed rice cereal if using. Store in an airtight container or in a plastic bag. If you have more than enough for 3 days, store the rest in the freezer.

Serve with milk or fruit juice and chopped fresh fruit in season.

Pancakes with fresh fruit, pecans, maple syrup and yogurt

These very delicate pancakes are suitable as a base for desserts as well as for breakfast.

Makes 4–5 pancakes, 7 in/18 cm in diameter

½ pint/250 ml/1¼ cups milk

1 egg

1 oz/25 g rice flour

2 oz /50 g corn flour

¼ oz /10 g soya flour

½ oz /10 g potato flour

a pinch of salt

olive oil or butter for frying

To finish

fresh fruit

maple syrup

pecan nuts

natural (plain) yogurt

Place the milk and egg in a liquidiser, add the dry ingredients and blend until smooth. For best results leave to stand for a few hours in the refrigerator. Stir the mixture before using, and while in use, because the flours are inclined to sink.

Heat a frying pan (skillet) and brush with oil or butter. Pour on some of the pancake mixture and swirl the mixture around the pan to make a thin delicate pancake. When it is cooked underneath, turn it over. When the second side is cooked lift out the pancake. Repeat the process until all the batter is used up. Keep the pancakes hot by placing them between plates over a pan of simmering water.

Arrange the pancakes, fruit, syrup, yogurt and a few pecan nuts decoratively on a plate and serve.

Variations

Fill with prunes or stewed apple and natural (plain) yogurt.

Fill with fried mushrooms and a little half-fat crème fraiche.

Top with grilled (broiled) tomatoes and grated cheese and flash under the grill (broiler).

Top with a berry compote, and serve with natural (plain) yogurt or a little half-fat crème fraîche.

Serve with natural (plain) yogurt, honey and toasted sunflower seeds.

Add chopped herbs (thyme, parsley, or chives) to the batter before cooking.

Filled tortillas

The linseeds and bran add fibre to these tortillas.

Makes about 5 pancakes, 6 in/15 cm in diameter

For the batter
1 dstsp linseeds, ground
3 oz/75 g brown rice flour
1 oz/25 g medium maize meal
1 dstsp rice bran
1 egg
½ pint / 250 ml/1¼ cup milk
a pinch of salt
butter or olive oil for frying

For the filling
olive oil for frying
5 bacon rashers (slices) chopped
1 onion, peeled and chopped
2 cloves garlic, peeled and crushed
1 red bell pepper, chopped
10 mushrooms, cleaned and sliced
1 dstsp fresh thyme, chopped

To finish

2 oz/50g cheddar cheese, grated
1 tblsp parsley, chopped, for garnish

Blend the batter ingredients thoroughly. Stir the batter well before and during use. Cook as for pancakes on a hot buttered frying pan (skillet). Keep the tortillas hot between plates over a saucepan of simmering water.

To make the filling, heat a little oil in a pan. Add the bacon if using. Add the chopped onion and garlic and cook gently without colouring. Add the pepper and mushrooms and continue to cook. Finally, add the thyme.

Divide the filling between the pancakes. Fold each pancake over the filling and sprinkle with the grated cheese. Decorate with chopped parsley and serve.

Potato pancakes

These are very tasty and very quick to prepare.

Makes 7–8 small pancakes, 3 in/7.5 cm in diameter

8 oz/200 g potatoes, peeled	1 ½ tblsp cornflour/maize flour
1 oz/25 g onion, finely chopped	1 egg
¼ tsp salt	¾ tblsp olive oil

Grate the potatoes manually or use a food processor. Add the onion to the grated potato. Mix the salt with the flour and add this to the potato mixture together with the egg. This must all be done just before cooking as the potato goes brown quickly.

Use enough oil to coat the bottom of the frying pan (skillet) and heat. Take a rounded tablespoon of the mix, place it in the pan and flatten it to a pancake about 3 in/7.5 cm in diameter. Cook each pancake for 2–3 minutes on the first side or until it turns reddish brown. Turn the pancake over and cook on the second side for another 2–3 minutes or until it is cooked. The pancakes can be kept hot in the oven.

Serve with grilled (broiled) bacon and tomatoes.

Variations

Top with grated cheese, flash under the grill (broiler) and serve with a side salad for a very satisfying lunch

Top with creamed mushrooms and lots of chopped parsley.

Serve with one of the savoury fillings suggested on page 43.

Rice bran pancakes with spicy apple, natural yogurt and honey

Makes 6–7 pancakes, 7 in/18 cm in diameter

For the batter

4 ½ oz/110 g rice flour

½ oz/10 g rice bran

½ tsp baking powder

a small pinch of salt

3 fl oz/75 ml/6 tblsp water

4 fl oz/100 ml/½ cup buttermilk

3 eggs

olive oil for frying

For the filling

2–3 eating apples, washed and
  cored

2 oz/ 60 g/½ stick butter

a pinch of ground clove *or* cinnamon

To finish

a drizzle of honey or maple syrup

1 tub of natural (plain) yogurt

Combine the ingredients for the batter and blend using a food processor, blender or whisk. Heat some oil in the frying pan (skillet) and place 2 table-spoons of the mixture on the pan and cook until golden underneath. Then flip over to cook the other side.

To make the filling slice the apple and fry in a little butter over gentle heat in a frying pan (skillet) for about three minutes. Sprinkle with the spice. Turn the slices over in the pan and cook for a few more minutes.

Fill the pancakes with the apple, drizzle with honey or maple syrup and serve with natural (plain) yogurt.

Other pancake fillings

Goats' cheese with roasted peppers, pesto and pine nuts.

Roasted pecan nuts with maple syrup and yogurt.

Grilled (broiled) bacon and tomatoes.

Beans in tomato sauce.

Drop scones

These are great in an emergency as they can be made very quickly.

Makes about 8 scones

4 oz/100 g rice flour

1 oz/25 g potato flour

½ oz/10 g maize flour

½ oz/10 g soya flour

½ tsp wheat-/gluten-free baking
  powder

1 tsp unrefined caster sugar (super
  fine sugar)

a pinch of salt

1 egg

6 fl oz/150 ml/¾ cup milk

butter for frying

Mix all the dry ingredients together in a bowl. Put the egg and milk into a food processor or liquidiser. Switch on and gradually add the dry ingredients. The mixture should be like pouring double (heavy) cream.

Heat a heavy-based frying pan (skillet) and place a knob (teaspoon) of butter in it. When the butter has melted, pour on the batter until it is about 3 in/ 7.5 cm in diameter. When the bottom is cooked (it will be brown), turn the scone over to cook the other side. Keep the scones hot in the oven.

Serve hot with butter and jam, marmalade or honey.

Spanish omelette

Spanish omelette is a great dish as it can be served cold or hot. It is best made thick like a cake. Serve it with salad and baked potato for a really satisfying meal. The Spaniards love to bring wedges of it on picnics. When it comes to variations of this dish, you are limited only by your imagination. Use such vegetables as: courgette (zucchini), onions, peppers of all shades, aubergines (eggplants), spinach and, of course, don't forget herbs and garlic. In Lisbon I remember having a most delicious omelette with salt cod which was just another variation.

Serves 2

1 large potato, peeled and chopped into small dice or a left over cooked potato, peeled and chopped into small dice

olive oil

½ red bell pepper, cored and chopped and/or 1 small onion, peeled and chopped

3 eggs

salt

freshly ground black pepper

In a small non-stick frying pan (skillet), fry the potato over medium heat without browning until almost cooked. Add the pepper or onion if using, and continue to cook until both potato and peppers/onions are done. (It is very important to cook the vegetables thoroughly at this stage.)

Beat the eggs in a bowl and season with salt and pepper. Add the cooked potato mixture to the egg mixture and mix well. Now clean the pan with a piece of kitchen paper. Oil it lightly with olive oil and place the egg and potato mixture in the pan over medium heat. Tuck in the edges all round as the omelette begins to set. If you like you can turn the heat down to low at this stage and cover the pan with a lid.

When the omelette is set, invert it onto a flat plate and slide it back onto the pan with the cooked side uppermost. Continue to cook until the underside is done.

Corn scramble

Serves 2

2 tsp of butter	1 tblsp chopped chives
3 fists of frozen sweet corn	salt
3 free range eggs	freshly ground black pepper
2 tblsp milk	

Melt the butter in a saucepan. Add the sweetcorn and stir. Put the lid on and sauté gently until the corn is warmed through.

Beat the eggs and add the milk, chives, salt and pepper. Add the egg mixture to the sweetcorn stirring all the time until the eggs scramble lightly. Remove from the heat.

Serve in moulds: place a large oiled scone cutter on the serving plate. Pile in the scrambled egg, press it down gently with the back of a spoon and remove the scone cutter.

Serve with grilled (broiled) tomatoes and/or mushrooms for breakfast, or for lunch try it with cress and a tossed mixed salad.

Seedy grilled (broiled) tomatoes

Serves 1

2 ripe tomatoes	salt
olive oil	freshly ground pepper
2 tblsp sunflower seeds or sesame seeds or pine nuts or a mixture of seeds and nuts	two slices special bread (see page 185)
	Garnish
	basil leaves

Slice the tomatoes across their 'equators'. Grill (broil) or fry them in olive oil. Meanwhile, roast the seeds or nuts by placing them (one variety at a time) into a dry saucepan over a medium heat. Watch them carefully, stirring all the time and remove immediately from the heat once they are golden in colour. Grind the sesame seeds roughly using a pestle and mortar, blender or liquidiser to get the greatest nutritional benefit.

Toast the bread. Place the tomato halves on the toast, sprinkle with the seeds and/or nuts and season with salt and pepper.

Variations

Top the tomatoes with grated cheddar cheese and flash under a grill (broiler)

Top the tomatoes with goats' cheese and pecan or pine nuts. Flash under the grill (broiler). Decorate with basil leaves.

Mashed potato savoury

Serves 1

left-over cooked mashed potato

a little milk to mix

1 tomato, sliced very thinly

slices of goats' cheese *or* your favourite cheese

a few torn basil leaves, for garnish

Re-heat the mashed potato in a saucepan, with a little milk if necessary. Turn on the grill (broiler) so that it is good and hot.

Place the hot mashed potato into a shallow individual heat-proof serving dish. Place the slices of tomato on top of the potato. Place under the grill (broiler) for about a minute. Remove and top with the cheese slices.

Return to the grill (broiler) until the cheese is golden and bubbling.

Garnish with the basil leaves and serve.

'We are meant to move towards whatever gives us fulfilment, personal growth and freedom.'

Christiane Northrup

Stocks and soups

When I was a youngster there was always a stockpot in the slow oven of the Aga in winter. I give some recipes here for homemade stocks, which are ideal for soups and certain sauces. However, few of us nowadays have time to make stock and though cubes and bouillon powder are not the same, you will be able to make very good soups with them. Wheat and/or gluten are often used as ingredients in stock cubes and bouillon powders, so do read the labels. In general, stock cubes and bouillon powders are very high in sodium and are not suitable for those on a low sodium diet. (However, some stock cubes and bouillon powders are now being produced with reduced sodium.) If you are using ordinary stock cubes or bouillon powders, you will have plenty of salt without adding any more.

If you are taking the trouble to make stock, make it in bulk and store it in convenient quantities in the freezer. Use frozen stock within one month, refrigerated stock within four days, or within one day in the case of fish stock. Butchers and fishmongers discard bones when preparing chicken and fish, so ask them to keep these bones for you. You can make stock from left-over bones or carcasses but the flavour is better if you use uncooked bones. If you are making stock for a special occasion, you could add a cup of dry white wine to the stockpot. Garlic is sometimes used as an ingredient in stock making. This is a matter of personal preference. If the stock is lacking flavour, reduce it to concentrate the flavour by boiling off some of the water. If you are unable to take dairy products, replace the milk in some of the soup recipes that follow with extra stock or non-dairy milk.

Chicken stock

4 lbs/2 kg bones *or* a mixture of
   bones and giblets
1 gal/4.5 litres/20 cups cold water
1 lb/400 g vegetables: onion, carrot,
   celery, leek

a few sprigs of thyme
a few parsley stalks
1–2 bay leaves
10–12 black peppercorns

Prepare the vegetables by peeling and roughly chopping the onions and carrots and washing, trimming and chopping the celery and leek.
Put all the ingredients into a large saucepan or stockpot. Bring to the boil. Skim the top if necessary. Turn down the heat and simmer for about 4 hours. Strain and cool.
Store in the refrigerator or freeze in convenient portions. Skim any fat off and use as required.

Vegetable stock

8 oz/200 g carrots, peeled and chopped

8 oz/200 g onions, peeled and chopped

8 oz/200 g celery, washed and chopped

8 oz/200 g leek, washed and chopped

a few sprigs of thyme

a few parsley stalks

1 bay leaf

12 black peppercorns

3 pints/1.5 litres/7½ cups cold water

Place all the ingredients in a large saucepan or stockpot. Bring to the boil, turn down the heat and simmer for 1–2 hours. Strain and cool. Refrigerate or freeze.

Fish stock

4 lb/2 kg fish bones, heads and skin (do not use oily fish or any gills)

2 tblsp olive oil

1 large onion, peeled and chopped

1 carrot, peeled and chopped

juice of ½ lemon

6 peppercorns

1 bay leaf

1 sprig of thyme

some parsley stalks

1 stick of celery

1 gallon/4.5 litres/20 cups cold water

Wash the fish bones. Heat the oil in a large saucepan or stockpot. Add the onion, the bones and the rest of the ingredients except the water. Cover and sweat for 5 minutes.

Add the water and bring to the boil, turn down the heat and simmer for 20 minutes. Strain and cool then refrigerate. Use as required.

Pea soup

Serves 4

1 tblsp olive oil

1 medium onion, peeled and
chopped

2 cloves garlic, peeled

1 nugget frozen spinach *or*
1 oz/25 g fresh spinach *or* the
greener leaves of a butterhead
lettuce

1 lb/400 g frozen peas

1 pint/500 ml/2½ cups vegetable *or*
chicken stock

1 tblsp chopped mint (optional)

1 tblsp chopped fresh parsley

salt

freshly ground black pepper

Garnish
a sprig of mint

Heat the oil in a large saucepan. Add the onion and garlic. Fry over gentle heat without colouring until the onion is soft and transparent. Do not allow the garlic to burn. Add the spinach, the peas and the stock. Bring to the boil and cook gently for about 10 minutes. Add the mint and parsley if using. Liquidise and bring back to the boil. Season to taste. If the soup is too thick, add more stock or water and serve with the mint garnish.

Carrot, red lentil and ginger soup

Serves 4

1 tblsp olive oil

1 medium onion, peeled and
chopped

½ oz/10 g fresh root ginger, peeled
and finely chopped

3 medium carrots, peeled and
chopped

1 oz/2 tblsp/25 g red lentils, washed

1½ pints/750 ml/3 ¾ cups vegetable
or chicken stock

salt

freshly ground black pepper

Garnish

1 tblsp chopped parsley

Heat the oil in a large saucepan. Add the onion and the ginger. Cook gently until the onion is transparent. Add the carrots, lentils and stock and bring to the boil. Simmer until the carrots are cooked. Liquidise—if it is too thick, just add more water or stock.

Season if necessary, garnish with the parsley and serve.

Variation

Add the grated zest of half an orange and replace some of the stock with the juice of the orange.

Mushroom soup

Serves 4

1 dstsp olive oil

1 medium onion, peeled and chopped

2 sticks celery (optional), trimmed and chopped

1 small leek (optional), trimmed and chopped

1 lb/400 g table mushrooms *or* a mixture of brown cap, oyster and breakfast mushrooms

1 pint/500 ml/2½ cups chicken *or* vegetable stock

1 medium potato, peeled and chopped

1 tsp fresh thyme leaves

½ pint/250 ml/1¼ cups milk or stock

salt

freshly ground black pepper

Garnish

1 dstsp chopped parsley

Heat the olive oil gently in a large saucepan, add the onion, celery and leek and sweat over low heat with the lid on.

When these vegetables have softened, add the mushrooms, turn up the heat and stir the vegetables until they have become very moist. Now add the stock, potato and thyme and bring the soup to the boil. Turn down the heat and cook until the potato is soft.

Add the milk or extra stock, liquidise and bring back to the boil.

Season to taste if necessary and serve garnished with parsley.

Leek and parsnip soup

Serves 4

1 medium leek

1 tblsp olive oil for frying

1 medium to large parsnip, peeled and chopped

1 medium onion, peeled and chopped

1 pint/500 ml/2½ cups vegetable or chicken stock

1 good bunch leaf coriander (cilantro)

½ pint/250 ml/1¼ cups milk *or* stock

salt

freshly ground black pepper

Remove the green tops from the leek. Cut it lengthways to wash in between the leaves. Chop it, discarding the root base.

Heat the oil in a large saucepan. Add the leek, parsnip and onion. Turn down the heat, put the lid on and sweat the vegetables for about 5 minutes. Now add the stock and cook until the vegetables are soft.

Add the coriander (cilantro) and liquidise.

Add the milk or extra stock, and salt and pepper if needed. Bring the soup back to the boil, adding a little more stock or water if it is too thick.

Leek and courgette soup

Make in the same way as leek and parsnip soup, but substitute a courgette (zucchini) for the parsnip and fresh basil for the coriander (cilantro). Use a small to medium potato to thicken the soup.

Celery and coriander (cilantro) soup

Celery and cauliflower are two vegetables which are outstanding for their potassium content and should often be included in the diet. They are especially good for anyone who is taking diuretics.

Serves 4

½ head celery, washed and chopped

1 medium onion, peeled and
  chopped

1 tblsp olive oil

1 pint/500 ml/2½ cups stock

1 medium potato, peeled and
  chopped

1 x 25 g bunch fresh coriander
  (cilantro), washed and chopped

½ pint/250 ml/1¼ cups milk *or* stock
  or water, to adjust thickness

salt

freshly ground black pepper

Fry the celery and onion in the olive oil in a large saucepan. Place the lid on the saucepan, turn the heat to low and sweat the vegetables for three or four minutes.

Add the stock and potato and cook until the vegetables are soft.

Reserve some of the chopped coriander (cilantro) for garnish and add the rest to the soup including the stalks.

Now liquidise the soup and adjust the thickness by adding extra milk or stock or water. Add salt and pepper if needed.

Garnish with the reserved coriander (cilantro) and serve.

Spicy chickpea and tomato soup

Serves 4

1 dstsp olive oil

1 onion, peeled and chopped

3 garlic cloves, peeled and crushed

1 tsp ground coriander (cilantro)

2 tsp ground cumin

1 lb/400 g can tomatoes in juice

1 lb/400 g can chickpeas, drained
   and rinsed

1 pint/500 ml/2½ cups chicken *or*
   vegetable stock

freshly squeezed lemon juice to taste

freshly ground black pepper

Garnish

half-fat crème fraîche

1 dstsp chopped parsley *or* leaf
   coriander (cilantro)

Heat the oil in a large saucepan and sweat the onion and garlic in the oil without burning.

Make a paste of the spices with a little water. Add the paste to the onion and garlic. Stir and cook over low heat for about 1 minute.

Add the tomatoes, chickpeas and stock, bring to the boil and then blend. Add lemon juice and black pepper to taste.

Serve garnished with a teaspoon of crème fraîche and chopped parsley or leaf coriander (cilantro).

Meal-in-one miso soup

This soup will only take about 11 minutes to prepare if you use white rice.

Serves 4

2 oz/50 g brown *or* white rice

½ red bell pepper, cut into julienne (fine strips)

½ red onion, peeled and finely sliced *or* 2 spring onions (green onions)

1 clove garlic, peeled and cut in two

½ large carrot *or* 1 small carrot, peeled and cut into julienne (fine strips)

1 in/2 cm piece root ginger, peeled and chopped

2 oz/50 g broccoli, broken into tiny florets

4 oz/100 g tofu, cut into small cubes (dolly mixture size)

4 dstsp unpasteurised miso

Cook the rice in 1 pint/500 ml/2½ cups water. When it is almost done, add the pepper, onion, garlic, carrot and ginger. Add ½ pint/250 ml/1¼ cups boiling water. Continue to cook for about 1 minute.

Now add the broccoli florets and cook for another minute. Stir in the tofu and finally the miso. Continue to heat gently but do not allow the soup to boil. Remove the garlic halves before serving the soup.

Easy seafood chowder

This soup is a meal in itself and very easy to prepare. It is based on a simple leek and potato soup.

Serves 4

1 leek, washed and chopped

1 onion, peeled and chopped

1 dstsp olive oil

1 medium potato, peeled & chopped

1 pint/500 ml/2½ cups fish or vegetable stock

½ pint/250 ml/1¼ cup milk or extra stock

4 oz/100g fresh salmon, skinned & boned, cut into ½ in/1 cm dice

4 oz/100g fresh cod, skinned and boned, cut into ½ in/1 cm dice

salt

freshly ground black pepper

2 tblsp chopped dill or fennel

Garnish (optional)

a little whipped cream

1 dtsp chopped parsley

Place the leek and onion in a large saucepan with the olive oil. Place the saucepan over moderate heat. Stir and cover. Reduce the heat to low and allow the vegetables to sweat for 4 or 5 minutes.

Add the potato and stock, bring to the boil and simmer until the vegetables are soft. Liquidise the soup. Now add the milk or extra stock, return the soup almost to boiling point and add the fish dice. Allow the fish to poach gently for about three minutes in the soup.

Season with salt and black pepper if required. Add the chopped fennel or dill and serve garnished if desired with a little cream and parsley.

Starters

Melon with orange and ginger 60

Melon with passion fruit 60

Green salad with rice cake croutons 60

Avocado guacamole with corn tortillas 61

Warm crisp bacon and walnut salad 62

Warm feta salad 62

Hot cheese-filled cherry tomatoes 63

Hot salads of salmon and mushrooms 64

If you are having a starter, choose one where the predominant ingredient is either vegetable or fruit. You will feel lighter after the meal and you will have boosted your fruit and vegetable intake.

Melon with orange and ginger

Melon is always a winner as it is so versatile and refreshing. Look for a ripe melon. To test it for ripeness press it at the flower end. If it gives under thumb pressure it is ripe. Use any type of musk melon but not water melon.
Serves 4

1 medium melon
1 juicy orange
1 in/2 cm piece fresh root ginger,
   peeled and grated

Garnish
orange slices

Cut the melon flesh into small pieces and place in a bowl. Juice the orange and pour the juice over the melon. Stir the ginger into the melon and orange mixture. Cover the bowl and leave it in the fridge for about half an hour for the flavours to blend. Serve in tall glasses garnished with slices of orange.

Melon and passion fruit

Mix melon pieces with the seeds of passion fruit. Chill and serve in glass bowls.

Green salad with rice cake croutons

Use a variety of salad leaves—choose from butterhead lettuce, iceberg lettuce, oak leaf lettuce, lollo rosso, lollo biondo, radicchio, red chard, curly endive, chicory, watercress, lamb's lettuce, cress and baby spinach. To add interest include a variety of herbs, especially the leafier kind such as rocket (arugula), basil, parsley, fennel, leaf coriander (cilantro) or lemon balm.

For the salad
Salad and herb leaves of your choice washed and torn

For the rice cake croutons

rice cakes, 1 or 2 per person

soft butter

grated parmesan, 1 dstsp per crouton

Preheat the oven to 180°C/350°F/Gas 4. Butter the rice cakes lightly. Dip the buttered sides in freshly grated parmesan. Place in the oven for about five minutes. When cool, the rice cakes should be really crispy and delicious. Dress the salad at the last minute with your favourite dressing. Serve with the croutons.

Avocado guacamole with corn tortilla chips

Make sure that the corn tortilla chips you use are wheat-/gluten-free.
Serves 4

2 ripe avocados

a squeeze of lemon or lime juice

2 tblsp fresh coriander (cilantro) leaves, chopped

1 tblsp red onion, peeled and finely chopped

1 tsp green chilli, chopped (optional)

a very little crushed garlic (optional)

salt

freshly ground black pepper

corn tortilla chips

Garnish

sprays of coriander (cilantro)

Mash the avocado flesh. Add lemon or lime juice to taste, the coriander (cilantro), most of the onion (reserving some for the garnish) and the chilli and garlic if using. Season to taste.

Place the guacamole in four ramekins, garnish with the onion and some coriander (cilantro) sprays and serve with corn tortilla chips.

Warm crispy bacon and toasted walnut salad

Serves 4

1 head of lettuce *or* a variety of
  lettuces
mixed herb leaves—fennel, coriander
  (cilantro), basil, parsley, oregano,
  rocket (arugula), chives etc.)
16 walnuts, chopped and toasted

lightly in a dry saucepan
8 rashers (slices) of smoked bacon,
  grilled (broiled) and chopped
dressing of your choice

Wash the lettuce and herbs. Tear the lettuce into bite-sized pieces with your hands. Place on a plate mixed with the herbs. Scatter the chopped walnuts and the hot crispy bacon over the top. Dress just before serving.

Warm feta salad

I often serve this as a main course. If you want to do likewise, just double the quantities and serve with a baked potato. You can buy marinated feta in specialist Mediterranean food shops but flavouring it yourself is very easy.

Serves 4

8–10 oz/200–250 g feta cheese
3–4 tblsp olive oil
1 clove garlic, peeled and
  crushed
1 bay leaf

1 tsp chopped thyme leaves or other
  herb
zest of ½ lemon
1–2 tblsp lemon juice
millet flakes

Cut the feta into cubes. Make a marinade by mixing the oil, garlic, bay leaf, thyme and the lemon zest and juice. Place the feta in the marinade, cover and leave it for several hours or overnight in the refrigerator.

Preheat the oven to 180°C/350°F/Gas 4. Remove the feta from the marinade and toss it gently in the millet flakes. Place the feta on a baking sheet and bake it in the oven for about 10 minutes.

If you prefer you could place the cheese under a preheated grill (broiler) until crisp, turning gently so as to crisp the underside.

Serve on plates garnished with salad leaves, roasted peppers, tomatoes and olives or with any salad ingredients of your choice.

Hot cheese-filled cherry tomatoes

This is a very colourful and appetising starter.

Serves 4

3–4 cherry tomatoes per person (red or yellow or both)

Boursin, or goats' cheese with herbs, or other soft cheese, 3 tsp per person

a few basil leaves

Garnish

cress or lettuce or salad

Pre-heat the oven to 200°C/400°F/Gas 6. Cut the tomatoes across their 'equators'. Scoop out the seeds with a teaspoon or melon baller and reserve. Fill the tomatoes with the cheese of your choice. Drizzle the tomato seeds and juice on top.

Place the tomatoes in an oiled baking dish and pop them in the oven for 5–10 minutes until they are heated through but not mushy.

Arrange the tomatoes decoratively on a plate with the basil leaves.

Garnish as desired and serve with toasted special bread, a potato scone or a herb scone.

Hot salad of salmon and mushrooms

Serves 4

2 oz/50 g fresh salmon per person

olive oil for frying

3–4 medium mushrooms per person,
   cleaned and sliced

a squeeze of lemon juice

a bunch of fresh coriander (cilantro),
   chopped

Remove the skin and any bones from the salmon and cut into ½ inch/1 cm cubes.

Heat the olive oil in a frying pan (skillet) or ridged pan. Fry the salmon. Remove from the pan when cooked, drain on kitchen paper and keep hot.

Fry the mushroom slices in the same pan and when cooked, add a squeeze of lemon juice to taste.

Place a bed of mushrooms on each plate and place the salmon cubes on top. Sprinkle the coriander (cilantro) over the salmon and mushrooms. Serve hot with some special bread or potato scones.

Chicken, lamb, beef and pork dishes

Chicken fillet parmigiano 66

Chicken Zaragoza 67

Zingy sesame lemon chicken 68

Tandoori chicken 69

Moussaka 70

Hash 72

Golden lamb casserole 73

Lamb-stuffed aubergine (eggplant) 74

Lamb burgers with melting hearts 75

Beef burgers 77

Korean beef stir-fry 78

Cottage pie 79

Escalope of pork steak with curried pears 80

Demi-veg stir fry pork 81

Chicken fillet parmigiano

My friend Catherine, who is a wonderful cook and connoisseur of Italian cuisine, inspired this dish. Though the chicken dish she described was cooked in the oven, I think it works really well fried in a little olive oil in the pan.

Serves 4

4 small chicken breast fillets

2–3 tbsp milk

½ tsp freshly grated nutmeg

2–3 tbsp freshly grated parmesan

olive oil for frying

Place the chicken breasts between two sheets of cling film and beat with a rolling pin or mallet to flatten them out to about ¼ in/0.5 cm in thickness. If you like, cut them into smaller pieces.

Mix enough milk with the nutmeg to marinate the chicken breasts and place the mixture in a shallow dish. Place the chicken in the marinade and leave in the fridge for at least 1 hour.

Remove the chicken from the fridge and drain each piece before coating in the grated parmesan.

Heat the olive oil in a pan. Fry the chicken, turning it once when it begins to turn a golden brown colour. Continue to fry until it is cooked through.

Serve with wheat-/gluten-free pasta, fresh tomato sauce or red bell pepper sauce and a green vegetable or side salad.

Chicken Zaragoza

This chicken dish is easy to make. For the family it is more economical to use a whole chicken rather than chicken breast fillets. Ask your butcher to portion the chicken, remove the breast meat from the bone and cut each leg into thigh and drumstick portions. Remove the skin and make stock from the bones and skin.
Serves 4

4 fl oz/100 ml/½ cup chicken stock

1 medium chicken, portioned and
    skinned *or* 4 chicken breast fillets

1 medium onion, peeled and chopped

2 cloves garlic, peeled and chopped

olive oil for frying

2 large red bell peppers, seeded and
    diced

½ pt/250 ml/1¼ cups red wine

2–3 bay leaves

4 large tomatoes, chopped or a 1 lb/
    400g can tomatoes

salt

freshly ground black pepper

Bring the stock to the boil. Add the chicken pieces and simmer for 15–20 minutes. Preheat the oven to 200°C/400°F/Gas 6.

Meanwhile, fry the onion and garlic in a little olive oil in a heavy casserole. Add the peppers and stir while frying over high heat. Add the wine, then the bay leaves, tomatoes and some of the stock the chicken was cooked in—there should be enough liquid to cover the chicken pieces. Bring to the boil. Finally add the chicken pieces. Give the mixture a good stir. Cover and place the casserole in the preheated oven for 20–30 minutes.

Serve with boiled brown rice and a green vegetable or green salad.

Zingy sesame lemon chicken

Serves 4

olive oil for frying

4 chicken breasts

2 dstsp honey

juice of 1 lemon

2 tsp grated fresh peeled root ginger

2 tsp tamari soy sauce

4 dstsp sesame seeds, crushed lightly

Garnish

slices of lemon

Heat the oil in a frying pan (skillet). Fry the chicken breasts on both sides until cooked and nicely browned. Remove from the pan and keep hot.

Meanwhile mix the honey, lemon juice, ginger and tamari soy sauce. Pour the lemon juice mixture into the pan. Bring to the boil, reduce the heat and cook the mixture to a syrup being careful not to burn it.

Return the chicken breasts to the pan and baste with the syrup. Spoon the sesame seeds over the chicken breasts. Baste again with the syrup.

Serve garnished with slices of lemon.

Tandoori chicken

Tandoori chicken is very easy to make. Commercially prepared Tandoori sauce or marinade may contain wheat and generally has food colouring added so it is best to make the marinade yourself. Prepare it the day before and marinate the chicken overnight. Serve the chicken with popadums, which are usually made from chick-pea (or gram) flour, but do check the label.

Serves 4

1 medium chicken, portioned and
   skinned

salt

¼ tsp chilli powder

1 tsp freshly ground black pepper

1 x 1 in/2 cm piece fresh root ginger,
   peeled and finely chopped

3 garlic cloves, peeled and crushed

2 tsp paprika (mild)

½ pt/250ml/1½ cups natural (plain)
   yogurt

2 dstsp olive oil

1 tblsp lemon juice

4 popadums

oil for frying

Garnish

4 wedges of lemon

4 sprigs of parsley

Pre-heat the oven to 230°C/450°F/Gas 8. Make slits through the flesh of the chicken and rub in a little salt. Mix together the chilli powder, black pepper, ginger, garlic, paprika, yogurt, oil and lemon juice. Pour the mixture over the chicken and place in a covered bowl in the fridge for 10–12 hours. Place the chicken on a wire rack over a roasting tin and cook until the juices run clear. It should take about 30 minutes.

For each person fry a popadum in oil in a frying pan (skillet). Fold it over while it is still in the oil. Tuck the chicken serving into the popadum and garnish with a slice of lemon and a sprig of parsley.

Tandoori chicken is delicious served with any of the following: a salad of cucumber, yogurt and mint, seasoned with pepper and salt; banana and yogurt salad or a side salad and plain boiled rice.

Moussaka

For informal dining this Greek dish has many advantages. Its flavour improves when prepared the day before it is needed, then all that remains to be done is to prepare the topping sauce, pour it over the moussaka and reheat it in the oven. Traditionally it is made from lamb, but it can be made from beef too. Shoulder of lamb is a good cut to use: ask your butcher to bone it and remove the fat. Mince it yourself in a food processor

Serves 4

1 dstsp olive oil

1 medium onion, peeled and chopped

2–3 cloves of garlic, peeled and
crushed

1–1¼ lb shoulder of lamb, trimmed of
the fat and minced

8 medium-sized ripe tomatoes or 4 very
big ripe tomatoes, chopped or a 14
oz/350 g can of tomatoes

1 dstsp chopped fresh oregano

1 dstsp chopped fresh thyme

salt and freshly ground black pepper

1 aubergine (eggplant), sliced

For the nutmeg topping

¾ oz/15 g cornflour or maize flour or
brown rice flour

½ pt/250 ml/1¼ cups milk

1 tsp freshly grated nutmeg

1 oz/25 g/¼ stick/2 tblsp butter

1 egg, separated

salt

freshly ground black pepper

Preheat the oven to 200°C/400°F/Gas 6.

Heat the oil in a saucepan and gently fry the chopped onion and garlic (do not allow the garlic to burn or you will spoil the taste of the dish). Transfer the cooked onion and garlic to the oven to keep hot.

Fry the meat in two batches until nicely browned. Keep the first batch hot while you prepare the second. Add the tomatoes (you may need a splash of water if you are using fresh tomatoes) and the onion/garlic mixture to the meat. Now add the chopped herbs, pepper and salt. Bring to the boil and allow to simmer for about 15 minutes while you cook the aubergine (eggplant).

Place the aubergine slices in a steamer and cook them until soft or brush them with olive oil and cook them under the grill (broiler).

Transfer a layer of the meat mixture to a pie dish or lasagne dish, followed by a layer of aubergine and continue in this way until the aubergine and meat are all used.

Place the moussaka in the preheated oven for about 30 minutes.

Meanwhile make the topping sauce.

Mix the cornflour, most of the nutmeg and milk until well blended. Transfer to a saucepan with the butter and continue to stir (a hand whisk is best for this) until the mixture thickens and boils. Stir over a low heat for one minute. Remove from the heat.

Whip the egg white until floppy. Beat the egg yolk into the sauce then add the pepper and salt. Now fold the whipped egg white into the sauce.

Cover the moussaka with the topping sauce and sprinkle the top with the rest of the grated nutmeg. Replace the moussaka in the oven and continue to bake until the topping is soufflé-like and golden.

Serve with a green or side salad and rice or baked potato.

Hash

It sounds like something illegal but this was our innocent name for Irish stew! It is one of my favourite dishes since childhood. My mother made a huge pot of hash every Saturday for our family of nine plus the men working on the farm. Apart from its taste, which is wonderful, it has the great advantage of being a one-pot meal. My mother served it with her own pickled red cabbage. If you want an easier option I suggest you try it with a good quality chutney.

Serves 4

1 lean gigot (stewing) lamb chop (trimmed of fat) per person (lamb shanks are also good)

1 large carrot per person, peeled and cut into large chunks

1 small onion per person, peeled and cut into leaves

1 stick of celery per person, cut in 3 or 4 pieces (optional)

a few sprigs of thyme

a bunch of parsley, washed and chopped

2–3 medium potatoes per person, peeled and cut in two

water

salt and freshly ground black pepper

Trim the fat from the chops. Wash them to remove any bone splinters. Place in a saucepan with the carrot, onion, celery, thyme and half the chopped parsley. Pour in cold water to almost cover the contents. Cover the saucepan. Turn on the heat and bring to the boil. Turn down the heat and simmer very slowly for about 30 minutes.

Now add the peeled potatoes. Season with salt and some freshly ground black pepper. Cover again and bring back to the boil. Now turn the heat down again and simmer until the potatoes are cooked, about 30 minutes.

When cooked there should be a delicious soup at the bottom of the saucepan. Serve the hash in soup plates garnished with the rest of the chopped parsley.

Golden lamb casserole

This casserole is bursting with fruity flavours. The orange juice provides vitamin C which helps to absorb the iron in the lamb.

Serves 5 or 6

1 dstsp olive oil

1 medium onion, peeled and chopped

1 clove garlic, peeled and crushed

1½ lb/600 g lean shoulder of lamb, cubed

4 carrots, peeled and chopped

¾ pt/375 ml/1¾ cups water

juice of 2 oranges

zest of 1 orange

8 dried apricots, washed, dried and chopped

2–3 tblsp fresh coriander (cilantro) chopped

salt

freshly ground black pepper

Pre-heat the oven to 180°C/350°F/Gas 4.

Heat the oil in a heavy-based ovenproof casserole. Add the onion and garlic and cook gently until soft but not coloured. Remove the onion/garlic mixture from the casserole and keep it hot.

Now brown the lamb cubes in two batches, keeping the first batch hot while browning the second. When the second batch is nicely brown add the first batch and the carrots, water, orange juice and zest, apricots, salt and black pepper. Stir well. Bring to the boil, cover and place in the preheated oven for 1 hour.

Add the coriander (cilantro) and serve with boiled brown rice or mashed potato and a green leafy vegetable.

Lamb-stuffed aubergine (eggplant)

This could also be made with beef but I have a preference for lamb. Again shoulder is a good cut, but make sure to trim off all the fat.

Serves 4

2 aubergines (eggplants)

olive oil

1 lb/500 g very lean lamb, minced

1 onion, peeled and chopped

2 cloves garlic, peeled and crushed

zest and juice of 1 lemon

2 dstsp chopped fresh herbs (a mixture of rosemary, sage and thyme is good)

3 tblsp chopped fresh parsley

2 tblsp currants washed, covered in hot water and soaked for 10 minutes

salt

freshly ground black pepper

4 tomatoes, sliced

Garnish

chopped parsley

Preheat the oven to 200°C/400°F/Gas 6. Split each aubergine (eggplant) in two along its length. Remove the flesh from each half, leaving about ½ inch/0.5 cm of flesh around the edge underneath the skin. Brush the hollowed out halves with olive oil on the inside and outside. Place them skin side up in a roasting tin in the oven while you prepare the filling.

Heat a little oil in a frying pan (skillet). Add half the minced lamb and fry until brown, then remove and keep hot while browning the second batch. Remove and keep the lamb hot while preparing the stuffing. Add the onion and garlic to the pan and cook over gentle heat until the onion is transparent.

Chop the aubergine (eggplant) flesh into small dice. Add it to the onion and garlic, turning the heat up slightly. Stir so that the vegetables do not burn. When the aubergine (eggplant) is soft, add the lemon zest and juice, the herbs, the currants and soaking liquid and the lamb mixture. Season to taste.

Remove the cooked aubergine (eggplant) shells from the oven and fill them with the prepared stuffing. Place the tomato slices on top of the stuffing.

Return the stuffed aubergines (eggplants) to the oven and cook for about 30 minutes. Serve sprinkled with parsley. They are very good served with mashed potato and a green vegetable or side salad.

Lamb burgers with melting hearts

Serves 4

1 lb/500 g shoulder of lamb, trimmed
    of fat and minced
1 onion, peeled and chopped
freshly ground black pepper
salt

1 dstsp chopped fresh thyme
1 dstsp chopped fresh mint
1 dstsp chopped fresh parsley
4 tsp Boursin, or other soft goats' or
    herb cheese

Mix all the ingredients except the cheese together. Shape with your hands into a ball. Make an indent in each ball and put a teaspoon of Boursin into the indent. Shape the mince back over the cheese so that it is hidden in the centre of each burger. Shape into a burger shape or use a burger press.

Grill (broil) on both sides until cooked through.

Serve with mashed potato and vegetable of your choice or with wheat-/gluten-free pasta accompanied by fresh tomato sauce or red bell pepper sauce.

'All things are possible and heaven is always listening.'

Caroline Myss

Beef burgers

To be sure you are getting the best of mince beef for your burgers, buy very lean beef pieces or stewing steak, trim the meat of all visible fat and mince it yourself in a food processor.

Serves 4

1 lb/500 g beef, minced

2 potatoes, peeled and grated

1 onion, peeled and finely chopped

1 tblsp chopped fresh parsley

1 tblsp chopped fresh thyme

salt

freshly ground black pepper

Preheat the grill/broiler. Mix all the ingredients together. Mould with your hands into burger shapes or use a burger press.

Cook very well under the grill (broiler) on the first side before turning. Continue to cook until there are no pink juices coming from the burger or pink meat in the middle.

Serve with yoqur favourite vegetable or side salad and mashed potato.

Korean beef stir-fry

This wonderful dish is easy to make, does not require unusual ingredients, can be prepared in advance and cooks very quickly. It's also great fun to use chopsticks, rice bowls and tamari soy sauce dishes instead of knives and forks. Your beef-loving friends will look for the recipe!

Serves 4

1½ hard pear, peeled and cored

2 cloves garlic, peeled

2 in/0.5 cm piece fresh ginger, peeled and coarsely chopped

4 tblsp tamari soy sauce

1¼ lb/500 g sirloin steak (for bigger appetites increase the quantity), cut into very thin strips

1 bunch spring onions (green onions), trimmed and sliced into 2 in/5 cm lengths

1 medium onion, peeled and cut into leaves

6 mushrooms, cleaned and thinly sliced

2 medium carrots, peeled and sliced on the diagonal into very thin strips

1 tblsp sesame seeds, roasted

2 tblsp olive oil

1 tsp unrefined sugar

Put the pear, garlic, ginger and tamari soy sauce into a blender and whizz until smooth. Put the meat in a bowl. Add the mixture from the food processor and all the vegetables. Mix in the sesame seeds, oil and sugar. Cover and leave in the refrigerator to marinate for up to 24 hours.

Preheat the oven to a low heat for keeping the meat hot. Heat a heavy frying pan (skillet) or wok, allowing it to get very hot. Remove the strips of meat from the marinade and cook them in a single layer. Turn them over when they are brown. Finish cooking the meat in this way and keep it hot in the oven while cooking the vegetables and marinade.

Place the vegetables in the pan and cook over a high heat, stirring all the time. Finally add any marinade left in the bowl and continue to stir over high heat until cooked. Add the meat to the pan and mix with the vegetables.

Serve with a bowl of rice and pair of chopsticks per person, a plate of lettuce leaves, julienne of vegetables and little dishes of tamari soy sauce. The diners make parcels of the beef, vegetables and rice with the lettuce and dip them in the soy sauce.

Cottage pie

Trim the beef and mince it yourself to ensure you get the best quality leanest beef for this recipe.

Serves 4

a little olive oil for frying

1 onion, peeled and chopped

1 clove garlic (optional), peeled and chopped

1 lb/500 g lean beef, minced

4–5 large very ripe tomatoes, finely chopped, or 1 can tomatoes (1lb/ 400 g) plus the juice

salt

freshly ground black pepper

1 tblsp chopped fresh parsley

1 tblsp chopped fresh thyme

salt and freshly ground black pepper

6–8 large potatoes, peeled and freshly boiled or steamed

1 knob/1 tbsp butter

2–3 tbsp milk

chopped parsley

Pre-heat the oven to 200°C/400°F/Gas 6. Heat the olive oil in a large frying pan (skillet). Add the chopped onion and garlic if using, and fry until transparent (being careful that the garlic does not burn). Remove from the pan and keep warm.

Fry the meat in small batches, stirring all the time, and make sure that it gets nice and brown. Remove each batch as it cooks and keep it warm with the onion. Fry the fresh tomatoes in the pan until soft, or add the canned tomatoes, and add the cooked onion and beef. Season with salt and pepper and add the fresh chopped herbs. If the mixture is very dry add a little water to make it juicy. Transfer the mixture to an ovenproof dish. Cover and cook in the pre-heated oven.

Mash the cooked potatoes and add the butter. Heat the milk in a saucepan and add it to the potato mixture. Season with salt and pepper and add plenty of chopped parsley if you wish. Beat the mash with a wooden spoon until it is fluffy then spread it over the meat mixture. Replace the dish in the oven and continue to cook until the potato is nicely brown on top.

Sprinkle with chopped parsley, and serve with a selection of vegetables or a side salad.

Escalope of pork steak with curried pears

One average size pork steak should be enough for three servings. Curried fruits make an excellent accompaniment to grilled (broiled) or cold meat, grilled (broiled) fish or vegetable burgers. The pears should be hard. You can also use peaches, nectarines or eating apples instead of pears. If you wish use a suitable curry paste rather than curry powder.

Serves 3

1½ pork steak

polenta for coating

black pepper and a little salt

olive oil for frying

For the curried pears

a little olive oil for frying

2 large pears (not very ripe) peeled, cored and neatly sliced

2 tsp wheat-/gluten-free curry powder

Trim the outside of the pork steak and cut it in three. Cut each third open with a sharp knife leaving a hinge. Place each piece of meat in turn between two pieces of cling film and beat with a rolling pin to flatten.

Season the polenta and toss each piece of pork in the polenta. Heat the oil and fry the pork in the oil until cooked. Meanwhile, prepare the curried pears.

Heat the oil in a pan. Add the sliced pears and cook on one side. Turn over to cook on the other. Mix the curry powder with a little water to make a thick paste. When the pears are warmed through, add the curry paste to the pan, toss the pears in the paste and serve.

Serve garnished with the curried pears. Red cabbage with apple juice and mashed potato would go very well with this dish.

Demi-veg stir-fried pork

Serves 4

1 lb/500 g very lean pork, trimmed of fat, cut into thin strips

2 dstsp cornflour

olive oil for frying

1 red onion, peeled and cut into leaves

2 carrots, peeled and cut very thinly on the diagonal

4 sticks celery, thinly sliced on the diagonal

1 red bell pepper, seeded, cut in thin strips

1 in/2 cm piece root ginger, peeled and finely chopped

3 cloves garlic, peeled and crushed

8 mushrooms, cleaned and finely chopped

1 packet bean sprouts, picked over, washed and drained

freshly ground black pepper

2 tblsp tamari soy sauce

a bunch of fresh green coriander (cilantro)

Preheat the oven for warming purposes.

Toss the meat in the cornflour. Heat the oil in a wok or frying pan (skillet) until very hot. Add the meat pieces. Cook on high heat, stirring all the time, until the pieces are cooked. Transfer the meat to the oven to keep hot.

Now add the onion, carrot, celery, bell pepper, ginger and garlic and continue stirring all the time. After about 3 minutes, add the mushrooms and continue to cook. The vegetables are cooked when they are *al dente* but not soft and mushy. When almost cooked, add the bean sprouts and the pork and cook for just 1 minute. Season with pepper and sprinkle the tamari soy sauce over the vegetable and pork mixture and add a splash of boiling water. (The water combines with the cornflour and the tamari soy sauce to produce gravy.) Stir again and add the coriander (cilantro).

Serve with boiled rice, millet or potatoes.

'Give to others what you want to receive:
love, support, appreciation, healing
and acknowledgement, and
you will get it back.'
Sanaya Roman

Fish dishes

Fresh fish is very much a convenience food as it is so quick and easy to prepare. The recipes taking the shortest time to prepare are the fish goujons, fried skate (ray) wings, and paella. These will also appeal very much to children. The other dishes need a little more time to prepare and make very good dishes for entertaining.

Salmon quiche

If you have difficulty handling the pastry, don't panic. Firstly, try rolling it out onto clingfilm (plastic wrap). Invert the dish over the pastry and lift the pastry on. If that doesn't work, simply press the pastry into the dish with your hands!

As quiche dishes vary in height as well as in diameter the basic rule for the amount of egg to milk is 1 egg and 1 egg yolk to every ¼ pint/125 ml/generous ½ cup milk. Alternatively, you could use 2 whole eggs to the same measure of milk. You will need a 7 inch/18 cm quiche dish or sandwich tin.

Serves 4–6

6 oz/150 g fillet fresh salmon
¼ pt/125 ml/ generous ½ cup milk
pastry/pie dough (see page 186)
bunch spring onions (green onions)
 washed, trimmed and chopped
olive oil for frying

1 tblsp fresh dill *or* fennel *or* chervil,
 chopped
1 egg and 1 egg yolk *or* 2 eggs
salt
freshly ground black pepper
1 oz/25 g cheddar cheese, grated

Preheat the oven to 200°C/400°F/Gas 6.

Poach the salmon in some of the measured milk until just cooked. Strain and keep the milk, adding it back to the remainder of the milk in the measuring jug. If needs be, bring the level of milk back up to the full measure.

Roll out the pastry and line the quiche dish. Fry the spring/green onions in a little olive oil until soft. Add the herbs and continue to cook for a further minute. Spread this mixture over the pastry. Flake the salmon and spread it evenly over the onion and herb mixture.

Beat the egg and egg yolk, or whole eggs, with the milk, salt and pepper until the mixture is smooth and even. Pour the egg mixture over the salmon. Sprinkle with the grated cheese. Bake in the oven until the egg is set and the top golden.

Serve with a side salad and baked potato.

Fish goujons

This is just a fancy name for fish fingers which are very popular with both adults and children. Ask the fishmonger to remove all the skin from the fish fillets. When you are well organised, the goujons are very easy to prepare.

Serves 2–3

12 oz/300 g fish (cod, haddock, hake, monkfish, plaice, lemon sole, etc.), skin removed

1 ½ oz/35 g brown rice flour, seasoned

1 egg, beaten with a fork

2 ½ oz /60 g millet flakes,

oil for frying

Garnish

lemon wedges to serve

Remove any bones from the fish. Cut the fish diagonally across the fillet into finger shaped pieces.

Put the seasoned flour in one bowl or plastic bag. Beat the egg and put it in another bowl and place the flaked millet in a third bowl or plastic bag.

Coat the fish pieces in the seasoned flour. Dip the floured pieces in the beaten egg and allow the egg to drain from each piece before coating in the millet flakes. Place the coated goujons on a plate and put them in the fridge to chill for a few hours. Shallow fry in olive oil. Drain on kitchen paper and serve with lemon wedges.

Fried skate (ray) wings

These are ideal for children as the flesh is very easily removed from the bones. They are also very quick and easy to prepare. It is essential for this dish to remove the skin from both sides of the ray wings—a good fishmonger will do this for you. When buying the wings, look for those that are nice and fleshy.

Serves 4

1 piece of fleshy ray wing (skin removed) per person

2–3 tblsp polenta (either coarse or medium), seasoned

salt

freshly ground black pepper

1 tblsp olive oil

1 knob/1 tblsp butter for frying

Garnish

lemon wedges

chopped parsley

Toss the ray wings in the polenta. Heat the olive oil and butter in a frying pan (skillet). Add the ray wings. When each browns on the first side turn it over to cook the other side. Make sure that the fleshier parts of each wing are cooked right through before removing them from the pan.

Serve with wedges of lemon and sprigs of parsley. These are good with mashed potatoes or chips and a selection of vegetables or a tossed salad.

Kebab of monkfish

This is a handy recipe as you can prepare it early in the day or the night before and leave it to marinate in the fridge. You will need 4 flat stainless steel skewers.

Serves 4

olive oil (about twice the quantity of the lime juice)

zest of ½ lime

juice of 1 lime

1 dstsp tamari soy sauce

1 clove garlic, peeled and crushed

1 x 1 inch/2.5 cm piece fresh root ginger, peeled and grated

1 bunch fresh coriander (cilantro) leaves

1 ¼ lb/560 g monkfish, trimmed and cubed (for big appetites you may need more)

1 red bell pepper, seeded and sliced into squares

1 green bell pepper, seeded and sliced into squares

1 red onion, peeled and cut into wedges

12 mushrooms, cleaned and dried

To make the marinade combine the oil, lime zest and juice, tamari soy sauce, garlic, ginger and coriander (cilantro) and mix well.

Add the monkfish, peppers, onion, ginger and mushrooms and coat in the marinade. Leave in the fridge to marinate for at least one hour, but preferably longer. Thread the fish and vegetables onto the skewers and grill (broil) until cooked, brushing occasionally with the marinade.

Serve with vegetable rice or creamed potatoes and a green vegetable.

Italian fish pie

This pie is equally delicious hot or cold and is very easily and quickly prepared. It can be made dairy-free by omitting the parmesan. You could use pesto sauce in place of the basil and olive oil.

Serves 4

8–10 medium potatoes, peeled and sliced into rounds about ¼ inch/0.5 cm thick

salt

1 oz/25 g fresh basil leaves and soft stems, washed

1 clove garlic, peeled

salt

4 tblsp olive oil

juice of ½ lemon

4 portions of cod or any fresh fish, skin removed

2 oz/50 g freshly grated parmesan

Garnish

8 black olives

Preheat the oven to 200°C/400°F/Gas 6.

Place the potato rounds in a saucepan. Sprinkle them with a little salt. Pour boiling water over them and bring them back to the boil. Simmer them until they are almost done. Then strain them in a colander.

While the potatoes are cooking, place the basil, the garlic and a little salt with the olive oil and lemon juice in the food processor or liquidiser. Whizz them together.

Pour a little of the oil and herb mixture on the bottom of a pie dish. Place half of the potatoes on top. Place the fish on top of the potatoes. Dress with a little more of the oil mixture. Place the rest of the potatoes on top of the fish. Sprinkle the rest of the dressing over them and finally the grated parmesan. Bake in the preheated oven for 30–45 minutes or until done.

Serve with a tossed mixed salad.

Paella

Emilia, my Spanish friend, loves paella just as much as I love Irish stew and for very similar reasons! It is very tasty, it can be prepared in a jiffy and there is only one saucepan to wash! Just double the quantities to serve four. If you use fresh fish it will be even nicer.

Serves 2

1 dstsp olive oil
1 small onion, peeled and chopped
1 clove garlic, peeled and crushed
1 red bell pepper, seeded and
 chopped
2 tomatoes, chopped
6 oz/150 g of white rice, washed and
 drained
a pinch of saffron strands, crushed

1 pt/500 ml/2 ½ cups water
2 fists frozen peas or 1 fist peas and 1
 fist sweetcorn
4 oz/100 g frozen prawns (shrimp)
4 oz/100 g or small tin tuna
freshly ground black pepper

Garnish
lots of finely chopped fresh parsley

Heat the olive oil in a saucepan. Add the onion and garlic and cook gently without colouring. Add the pepper and tomatoes and cook for a minute.

Now add the rice and stir to coat the rice in the oil. Add the saffron and the water. Stir and bring to the boil. Cover and turn down the heat so that it just simmers.

Put the peas (and sweet corn if using) in a bowl and pour some boiling water over them just to get rid of the ice. Drain.

In 10–12 minutes the rice will have soaked up the water and it will be time to add the peas, prawns and tuna. Cover again and leave to stand for about 5 minutes. Fork the fish, peas and black pepper into the rice.

Turn it out onto a hot serving dish and garnish with chopped fresh parsley.

'It is often the smallest, most anonymous acts which create the loudest thunder in the spiritual world.'

Thom Hartmann

Vegetarian dishes

In this chapter you will find a variety of dishes to suit the vegetarian diet. I have included recipes based on dairy products, eggs, pulses and nuts. Some, such as the Mediterranean gateau and the parsnip and hazelnut roulade, are time-consuming to prepare. Others such as cashew burgers or mushroom risotto can be prepared quickly. If you cook dried pulses in advance and freeze them, pulse dishes can be prepared even more quickly than their meat-containing equivalents.

Mediterranean gateau

This is a very elegant dish made of layers of pancakes alternating with layers of roast vegetables, goats' cheese and pesto sauce. It makes a terrific vegetarian dish for entertaining or for a festive occasion. It is well worth the effort. If you want to cut down on the oil you could replace the pesto with torn basil leaves.

You could roast the vegetables and make the pesto the night before, then refrigerate them until needed. You can also make the pancakes ahead of time. As you cook them, place them on a plate separated by pieces of greaseproof or parchment paper. When the pancakes are cool, cover them with a second plate and refrigerate.

The gateau could even be assembled and refrigerated in advance; then about 1½ hours before serving, cover it loosely with tin foil and place it in a preheated oven 180°C/350°F/Gas 4.

Serves 4

For the roasted vegetables

3 large peppers
1 medium aubergine (eggplant), sliced
2 red onions, peeled and sliced
4 large ripe tomatoes, thickly sliced
olive oil

For the pancakes

6 oz/150 g brown rice flour
2 oz/50 g medium maize meal
2 dstsp ground linseeds
2 dstsp rice bran
2 eggs
1 pint/500 ml/2½ cups milk

a pinch of salt

For the pesto

½ oz/10 g basil
4 fl oz/100 ml/½ cup olive oil
¾ oz/15 g freshly grated parmesan
½ oz/10 g pine nuts
1 clove garlic, peeled and crushed
   (optional)
a few twists of black pepper

To finish

8 oz/200 g goats' cheese
1 oz/25 g parmesan
1 tomato, sliced

Preheat the oven to 200°C/400°F/Gas 6. Brush the whole peppers, aubergine (eggplant) and onion slices with olive oil. Place them in a roasting tin and roast.

Brush the tomato slices with olive oil and add them to the roasting tin after about 20 minutes–they take only about 10 minutes to roast.

When the vegetables are ready, remove the tin from the oven. Peel the skin from the peppers, discard the stalks and seeds and cut the peppers into strips, reserving a few.

Make the pancakes—you need 4 large pancakes for three layers. Put all the ingredients in a liquidiser or food processor and blend until smooth. When you are cooking the pancakes stir the batter occasionally before pouring it into the pan. Keep the pancakes warm between plates over simmering water.

Make the pesto: place all the ingredients in the food proccessor and whizz. There should no need for salt as the cheese is very salty.

To assemble: place a pancake on a well greased baking tray or ovenproof plate. Put the cooked aubergine (eggplant) and onion on top, reserving a few pieces of onion. Spread a quarter of the goats' cheese and some pesto over the vegetables and lay another pancake on top. Put a layer of cooked tomatoes on top of the pancake and place another quarter of the goats' cheese and more pesto on top.

Place the third pancake on top of the tomato layer and place the sliced peppers on top, again reserving a few slices. Cover with another quarter of goats' cheese and some pesto.

Now add the remaining pancake and cover with the remaining goats' cheese. Garnish with the reserved onion and peppers and the uncooked tomato. Sprinkle with grated parmesan and drizzle with more pesto. Cover with tin foil and place in the preheated oven for an hour or more or until heated through.

Serve the gateau with a salad and baked potato or some of your favourite vegetables.

Mushroom risotto

This tasty vegetarian dish is very easy and quick to prepare. It is probably best served in individual dishes, for example, soup plates, topped with an attractive garnish and accompanied by a side salad or selection of cooked fresh vegetables.

Serves 3

2 oz/50 g/½ stick/¼ cup butter

1 onion, peeled and finely chopped

8 oz/200 g mixed mushrooms, cleaned and chopped

6 oz/150 g risotto rice washed and drained

1 pint/500 ml/2½ cups water or stock

6 fl oz/150 ml/¾ cup white wine

3 oz/75 g freshly grated parmesan cheese

lots of freshly chopped parsley

salt

freshly ground black pepper

Preheat the oven to 190°C/375°F/Gas 5.

Melt the butter in a casserole and sauté the onion until soft. Add the mushrooms and cook for about 3 minutes. Add the rice and stir to coat it in the butter. Now add the water or stock and the wine and season with salt and pepper. Bring to the boil, then cover the casserole and place it in the oven.

After about 20 minutes in the oven, remove the casserole and stir in the parmesan and most of the parsley. Replace in the oven and continue to cook for 10–15 minutes or until cooked.

Serve garnished with the reserved parsley and a few coarse parmesan shavings if liked.

Red kidney bean chilli

This chilli is very quick and easy to prepare if you cook the beans in advance, or use tinned beans. It is suitable for vegans.

Serves 6

1 tblsp olive oil

2 medium onions, peeled and chopped

2 cloves garlic, peeled and crushed

1 green bell pepper, seeded and chopped

1 tsp ground coriander

½ tsp ground clove

½ tsp ground allspice

2 tsp ground cumin

2 cans chopped tomatoes (2 x 1lb/ 400g)

1 small tin tomato purée

1 tblsp unrefined sugar

2 tsp dried oregano or 1 tblsp fresh oregano

1 very finely chopped chilli or ¼ tsp ground chilli

2 cups cooked red kidney beans

Heat the oil in a saucepan. Add the onion, garlic and pepper. Stir until they soften and do not allow them to burn.

Mix the spices with a very small amount of water to form a thick paste. Add the paste to the onion mixture and continue to cook while stirring for another minute or two. Add the tomatoes, tomato purée, sugar, oregano and chopped or ground chilli. Add the beans. Bring to the boil, cover and simmer gently for about half an hour.

Serve with nutty brown rice and a green vegetable or green salad.

Parsnip and hazelnut roulade

This dish is ideal for a festive occasion. It is time-consuming to prepare but with a bit of advance preparation it is easy to do.
Serves 4

For the stuffing

½ hazelnut stuffing recipe (see page 155).

Reserve a few roasted, chopped hazelnuts for sprinkling on the roulade.

For the filling

3 parsnips, peeled, chopped and steamed
a knob/1 tblsp of butter
2 tblsp fresh chives, snipped
salt
freshly ground black pepper

For the roulade

1½ oz/35 g butter
1½ oz/35 g rice flour

10 fl oz/250 ml/1¼ cups milk (for added flavour infuse the milk with a bay leaf, onion, peppercorns and mace)
12 oz/25–50 g cheddar cheese, grated
salt
freshly ground black pepper
3 eggs, separated

Make the filling: Mash or purée the parsnips. Add the butter and chives and season with a little salt and pepper.

Preheat the oven to 200°C/400°F/Gas 6.

Grease and line an 8½ x 12½ inch/22 x 32 cm Swiss roll tin. Use baking parchment rather than greaseproof paper.

Make the roulade: Melt the butter in a saucepan and add the flour. Cook while stirring for 2–3 minutes over gentle heat. Pour on the milk and whisk. Bring the sauce to the boil and continue to cook over gentle heat for 2–3 minutes. Stir in the grated cheese, a little salt and pepper and allow the mixture to cool slightly before whisking in the egg yolks.

In a clean glass bowl whisk the egg whites until they form soft peaks. Stir 1 tablespoon of the egg white into the sauce, then fold the rest in gently.

Sprinkle the stuffing over the base of the prepared Swiss roll tin. Spread the parsnip filling over the stuffing and then spread the roulade mixture over the filling. Sprinkle a few roasted and chopped hazelnuts over the roulade and transfer it to the oven.

Bake for about 25 minutes near the top of the oven, then turn out onto more parchment paper and roll up. Transfer to a serving plate and garnish as desired. Serve immediately with lots of salad.

Variations

These are endless. Here are a few examples:

Add some blanched, chopped and drained spinach and a little nutmeg to the roulade mixture before folding in the beaten egg white.

Fill with leek, carrot and herb purée or minted pea purée, or spinach and pine nuts, or creamed garlic mushrooms.

Use apricot and ginger stuffing (see page 154) and fill with carrot and ginger purée.

Baked beans

For this recipe you can use any of a variety of beans. Try black eye beans, haricot beans, flageolet beans or any other kind that takes your fancy.

Serves 4

8 oz/200 g dried haricot or other
   beans, soaked overnight
1 onion, peeled and studded with
   about 20 cloves
1 bayleaf
1 tblsp olive oil
1 onion, peeled and chopped
1 medium carrot, peeled and chopped
1 leek, washed and chopped
6 mushrooms, cleaned and chopped
1 clove of garlic, peeled and crushed

4 large ripe fresh tomatoes, chopped
1 pear, peeled and chopped
1 tblsp chopped fresh thyme
1 tblsp chopped fresh oregano
1 tsp chopped fresh summer savoury
   (optional)
1 tsp paprika
½ pint/250ml/1¼ cups stock
salt
freshly ground black pepper
chopped parsley

Rinse the beans in fresh water. Place them in a large saucepan with the clove-studded onion and a bayleaf. Cover with cold water and bring to the boil. Boil rapidly for 10 minutes and then turn down the heat and simmer the beans until they're tender. This could take up to 1½ hours depending on the type and freshness of the beans. Alternatively use the gas reducing method (see page 21) and reserve the onion and bayleaf for the second boiling. When the beans are cooked strain them, put them to one side and reserve the cooking liquid. Discard the onion and bay leaf.

In a clean saucepan or heavy-based casserole heat the olive oil and add the chopped onion, carrot, leek, mushrooms and garlic. Cook slowly, stirring occasionally to prevent burning. Add the tomatoes, pear, herbs (except for the parsley) and paprika. Season with salt and pepper and add the stock. Cover and cook until the carrots are tender. Add the cooked beans and chopped parsley. Stir well. A little of the cooking liquid can be added if necessary to adjust thickness.

Heat through and serve with boiled brown rice and a green salad.

Variations

Top the finished dish with a crumble topping made from butter, millet flakes and brown rice flour and cook in the oven until the crumble is golden.

Top with mashed potato and serve in individual dishes or in one big pie dish.

Twice-baked potatoes

This is a very good dish served with salad for a special lunch. Once the potatoes are stuffed they can be refrigerated and heated through when required. If you are not a vegetarian you can include some bacon rashers (slices) in the filling.

Serves 4

4 very large potatoes

olive oil

4 bacon rashers (slices) (optional)

1 onion, peeled and finely chopped

1 clove garlic, peeled and finely
   chopped

1 red bell pepper, seeded and
   chopped into small dice

8 mushrooms, cleaned and chopped

a knob/1 tblsp butter

4 oz/100 g cheddar cheese,

1 tblsp parsley

1 dstsp fresh thyme

salt

freshly ground black pepper

4 sprigs fresh thyme

Pre-heat the oven to 200°C/400°F/Gas 6. Wash and dry the potatoes and brush lightly with oil. Put a cut around the potato so that the top can be easily removed when the potato is cooked. Bake in the oven until cooked. Depending on size, this will take 45–60 minutes. (For the non-vegetarian version, grill/broil the bacon slices, transfer them to a plate and keep them warm.)

Now fry the onion in the oil until soft. Add the garlic, red pepper and mushrooms and cook until soft.

Remove the cooked potatoes from the oven. Cut the lids off. Scoop the potato flesh from the potato shells. Mash with a potato masher. Add the vegetable mixture, butter, most of the cheese, (the rasher if using), the herbs and season with salt and pepper. Fill the empty potato shells with the mixture, top with the reserved cheese and a sprig of thyme, and replace the tops. Put the stuffed potatoes back into the oven and heat through. This will take about 20 minutes in a preheated oven.

Vegetarian rosti

A rosti consists of a base made of potatoes and a topping, traditionally made from the produce of the Swiss farms: cheese, bacon, sausages, eggs, onions and potatoes. I came across rostis in a restaurant in Interlaken. All of them were served in the frying pan (skillet) in which they were cooked. This was a very clever idea as rosti breaks up easily when you attempt to remove it from the pan. (Though you can be very successful if you slide it out onto a large plate). So if you are looking for perfection I'm afraid you will need a frying pan (skillet) per person. Otherwise make it in a big pan and portion it out as best you can. If you are not a vegetarian, try rosti topped with bacon rashers (slices) chopped and fried until crisp or wheat-/gluten-free sausages, fried onions, Emmenthal cheese and a fried egg.

Serves 2 or 3

2 medium red onions, peeled and cut in quarters

6 tomatoes, halved

olive oil

6 potatoes, peeled and sliced very thinly

4 oz/100 g Emmenthal

Garnish
basil leaves

Pre-heat the oven to 200°C/400°F/Gas 6. Brush the tomatoes and onion quarters with olive oil, place them in an oven-proof dish and put them in the oven to roast.

Heat some oil in a large frying pan (skillet) and add the potatoes, separating the very thin slices from one another. Press them down to form a thick, flat layer. Cook over low heat until the potatoes are cooked through and coloured underneath.

Now turn the pan upside-down very carefully onto a flat plate. Do this over the sink or drainer, and with the plate tilted away from you, so that you do not get burned with the oil. Return the potatoes to the pan by sliding them back, pale side down. Continue to cook over gentle heat until the underside is coloured.

When the potatoes are cooked, place the roasted tomatoes and onions on top. Cover them with the grated Emmenthal which should melt down into the potatoes. To speed up the melting, you could flash the rosti under the grill (broiler) for a few minutes. Garnish with torn basil leaves and serve.

Variations

Try other toppings on your rosti such as:

Fried mushroom topped with grated cheese.

Any left over baked beans from the recipe in this chapter. Top the beans with grated cheese and garnish with lots of parsley.

Roasted aubergine (eggplant), courgette (zucchini), red bell pepper and red onion with gruyere or cheddar.

Artichoke hearts, chopped semi-sundried tomatoes, roasted tomatoes, olives, Emmenthal, parmesan and fresh basil.

Fried rings of eating apple topped with Emmenthal or gruyere.

A mixture of stir-fried onions, garlic, red bell peppers, mushrooms and herbs topped with fried tofu previously marinated in a mixture of tamari soy sauce, dry sherry or rice wine, garlic, ginger and a splash of roasted sesame oil.

Roasted Mediterranean vegetables with olives, topped with feta marinated in olive oil, lemon juice, garlic and fresh herbs and flashed under the grill (broiler).

Steamed buttered spinach, poached egg and grated cheese.

Puy (French green) lentil stuffed aubergine (eggplant)

I was inspired to create this dish having tasted a similar one in Tilley's Bistro in Bath. If you want to be kind to your arteries and boost your iron and magnesium intake, Puy (French green) lentils are the answer. They are considered the most special of all legumes.

Serves 4

4 oz/100 g puy (French green) lentils

2 aubergines (eggplants)

olive oil

3 oz/75 g currants *or* dried apricots

1 onion (a red onion gives great colour), peeled and chopped

3 cloves garlic, peeled

2 tsp ground coriander (cilantro)

1 bunch fresh coriander (cilantro)

zest of ½ lemon

juice of 1 lemon

Garnish

coriander (cilantro) sprigs

lemon slices

Wash the lentils and place them in a saucepan. Cover them with water and bring to the boil. Turn down the heat and simmer them until tender. Drain and set aside.

Pre-heat the oven to 200°C/400°F/Gas 6.

Cut the aubergines (eggplants) in half and remove the flesh, leaving just a rim of flesh underneath the skin. Chop the flesh very finely and leave to one side. Brush both sides of the aubergine shells with olive oil and place them in a roasting tin, skin side up, then bake in the oven while you continue the preparation. Wash the dried fruit and leave to soak by just covering with hot water.

Heat a little oil in a frying pan (skillet) and add the onion and the garlic. Cook without colouring for about 3 minutes. Now add the aubergine flesh and fry gently, stirring all the time until it softens a little. Add the ground coriander (cilantro) and stir for another minute.

Chop the leaf coriander (cilantro), reserving a few sprigs for decoration, and add with the lemon juice, zest, lentils, currants, and soaking water. Season with salt and pepper. Cover with a tight fitting lid. Turn the heat to very low and allow to cook very gently for a few minutes until the aubergine is soft.

Remove the shells from the oven and fill them with the mixture. Cover the stuffed shells with greaseproof or parchment paper and tin foil and cook for another 25–30 minutes until the mixture is heated through and the aubergine flesh is thoroughly cooked. Remove the shells from the oven and place them carefully on individual plates. Garnish with coriander (cilantro) sprigs and slices of lemon. Serve with nutty brown rice and a green vegetable or tossed salad.

Cashew burgers

These cashew burgers are wonderful served with mango salsa.

Serves 4

1 medium onion, peeled and finely chopped	2 rounded tblsp finely chopped fresh coriander (cilantro)
olive oil for frying	1 tsp chopped fresh parsley
6 oz/150 g mushrooms, cleaned and finely chopped	1 tsp chopped fresh thyme
1 carrot, peeled and grated	1 tblsp tamari soy sauce
8 oz/200 g mashed potato	freshly ground black pepper
6 oz/150 g cashew nuts, finely chopped	½ small egg, lightly beaten
	polenta *or* rice flour for coating

Fry the onion in olive oil over medium heat until soft. Add the mushrooms and carrot and cook until soft. In a large bowl combine the potato, chopped nuts, the cooked vegetable mixture, herbs, tamari soy sauce and black pepper.

Allow the mixture to cool slightly before adding the beaten egg. Divide the mixture into eight portions and shape them into burgers and dust with rice flour or polenta. Refrigerate the burgers if you are not cooking them immediately.

To cook, heat some olive oil in a frying pan (skillet) and fry the burgers until they are golden brown, then turn them over to cook the other side.

To make this a vegan dish, omit the egg and bake the mixture in an oiled pie dish for 30 minutes in a medium oven.

*'As you look for the best in everyone,
so strength will flow into you,
and peace will dwell in you.'*

The Source Of All Our Strength

Potato, rice, polenta and millet side dishes

Potatoes, rice, polenta and millet can each be used to provide the main ingredient for a wonderful variety of side dishes. These foods provide complex carbohydrate in the diet. Together with special breads they are the best source of energy for those who must avoid wheat and/or gluten.

Olive oil baked potato

These potatoes can be used to accompany a meat, fish or vegetarian main course. You can also use them to make twice-baked potatoes.

1 large potato per person, washed
  and dried

olive oil to coat
salt

Preheat the oven to 200°C/400°F/Gas 6. Cut a cross through the skin on each potato. Pour a little olive oil onto your hands and rub the potatoes with the oil to coat them completely, then sprinkle them with a little salt and rub it in.
Place the potatoes in a roasting tin and bake them for about 45 minutes.
To break a baked potato open, hold it with a tea towel, with the cross side up, and squeeze it gently, pushing the underside up.
Serve plain or with butter, garlic butter, whipped cream or natural (plain) yogurt to which has been added a little garlic and fresh herbs.

Chips without the chip pan

This is a healthier way of making chips than deep-frying as only a little olive oil is used and that only once.
Serves 4

2 tblsp olive oil
4–6 potatoes, peeled and cut into thick
  chips

boiling water
salt

Preheat the oven to 250°C/500°F/Gas 9. Pour some olive oil into a roasting tin, put the tin in the oven and let the oil get really hot.
Place the chips in a saucepan. Pour boiling water over them, add a little salt and bring the water back to the boil. Allow the chips to boil for one minute, then strain them in a colander.
Dry the chips very well in a clean tea towel then toss them in the hot olive oil—they should fit in a single layer in the tin. Sprinkle the chips with a little salt.

Place the roasting tin on the top shelf of the oven if it does not have a fan. The chips will take about 20 minutes to cook.

Roast potatoes

3–4 pieces of peeled potato per person

salt

olive oil

Preheat the oven to 230°C/450°F/Gas 8. Leave small potatoes whole and cut any bigger potatoes into chunks about the same size as the small potatoes. Place the potatoes in boiling salted water. Bring back to the boil and boil for 1 minute. Strain. Shake the potatoes in the saucepan to dry them off.

Heat some olive oil in a roasting tin, then add the potato pieces, and baste them with the oil to coat each piece. Roast them for approximately 30 minutes.

Variation: Herb-scented roast potatoes

These are especially good with rosemary. Proceed as for the previous recipe but flavour the oil by whizzing it with some herb leaves and a little salt in a food processor.

Potato cakes

Makes about 8 cakes

8 medium potatoes, peeled and boiled

2 oz/50 g/½ stick/¼ cup butter

1 onion, peeled and sliced

1 egg, beaten or 1 egg white, beaten

1 tblsp chopped fresh chives

salt

freshly ground black pepper

2 tblsp rice flour, ground rice or polenta for coating

olive oil for frying

Mash the potatoes. Melt the butter, then cook the onion in the butter until soft. Mix the potato, onion, egg and chives and season to taste. Divide the mixture into eight and shape into cakes with your hands. Coat each cake in brown rice flour, ground rice or polenta then shallow fry in olive oil.

Mock goose

A potato dish in its own right, this is also the traditional stuffing for a goose.

Serves 4

2 lb/1 kg freshly cooked mashed
   potato

1 oz/30g/¼ stick/2 tblsp butter

1 onion, peeled and chopped

1 medium to large cooking apple,
   peeled and finely chopped

4 chopped sage leaves

2 dstsp chopped fresh thyme leaves

salt

freshly ground black pepper

Garnish

2 tblsp finely chopped parsley

Prepare the mashed potato and keep it warm.

Melt the butter in a saucepan. Add the onion and cook gently—do not allow it to colour. Add the apple, sage and thyme, stir and continue cooking over a low heat until the apple is cooked. Add the apple mixture to the mashed potato and mix well. Season with salt and pepper and serve garnished with finely chopped parsley.

Citrus potato mash

The tangy taste of this potato dish makes it ideal to serve with either roast pork or roast duck.

Serves 4

1 small orange (washed thoroughly)

a pinch of bread (baking) soda

1 lb/500 g potatoes, peeled

1 small onion, peeled and finely
   chopped

a knob/1 tblsp of butter

salt

freshly ground black pepper

Garnish

lots of freshly chopped parsley

Place the orange in a small saucepan, cover with water, add the bread (baking) soda, cover and bring to the boil. Turn down the heat and simmer for 45 minutes.

Meanwhile, boil the potatoes then mash them. Fry the onion in the butter. When the orange is ready chop it finely, add it to the onion then add the mash and season to taste. Pile the mixture into an ovenproof dish and place it in the oven to heat through.

Alternatively heat the mash by placing it in the pan in which the onion was cooked over a low heat and stir well until warmed through.

Sprinkle with the parsley and serve.

Variation: Leek mash

Fry a chopped leek in butter. Add to the mash. Season to taste.

Potatoes boulangère

This is a very tasty way of serving potatoes without using any fat. You do, however, need to make good flavoursome stock. I have found Rooster potatoes good for this dish as they do not soak up as much liquid as Golden Wonders.

Serves 2–3

½ pint/250 ml/1¼ cups good chicken *or* vegetable stock

1 lb/500 g potatoes, peeled and very thinly sliced

2 medium onions, peeled and cut into rings or slices

3–4 sprigs of fresh thyme or 1 tsp dried thyme

salt

freshly ground black pepper

Remove any fat or oil from the surface of the stock and bring it to the boil. Preheat the oven to 220°C/425°F/Gas 7. Place some potato slices on the bottom of a deep ovenproof dish. Place a layer of the sliced onion on top. Place the thyme on top of the onion. Continue layering until all the vegetables are used up. Sprinkle with salt and pepper and pour over the boiling stock. (Using boiling stock will reduce the cooking time in the oven.) The stock should just barely cover the potatoes. Cover the dish. Cook for 1–1½ hours, adding more stock if necessary. Press the potatoes down occasionally during cooking.

Plain boiled rice

The easiest way to boil rice is to follow the packet instructions. If you have not found these reliable in the past the following tips may be helpful.

♦ American or Australian packaged rice needs no washing or soaking. Wash all other kinds.

♦ Use a pot with a tight fitting lid. If the lid doesn't fit tightly, use baking parchment inside the lid.

♦ Long grain rice, when soaked for 30 minutes, needs only one and one-third parts of liquid to one part of rice for cooking. When not soaked, use one and a half parts of liquid to one part of rice when cooking.

♦ The texture of brown rice improves with soaking. Use two parts liquid to one of brown rice for soaking. After soaking brown rice for an hour, do not drain it but cook it in the same water for 35 minutes.

♦ Use a little salt in the water when cooking any kind of rice except when it is for a Chinese meal.

♦ When brown or white rice is cooked, let it stand with the lid on for 10 minutes in a warm place.

♦ If you cook a lot of rice, consider buying a rice cooker and follow the manufacturer's instructions.

Vegetable rice

This makes a very colourful and tasty accompaniment to grilled (broiled) fish or meat or vegetarian rissoles or burgers. Use whatever vegetables you like—this recipe is only a guide. Though I have fried the vegetables here you could steam them if you prefer.

Serves 4

10 oz/250 g rice

1 dstsp olive oil

1 medium red *or* plain onion, peeled and chopped

½ red bell pepper, seeded and finely chopped

½ green or yellow pepper, seeded and finely chopped or slices of mangetout

2 cloves garlic, peeled and crushed

1 stick celery, finely chopped

4 tblsp frozen corn

4 tblsp frozen peas

Garnish

fresh parsley, chopped

Boil the rice with a little salt in the water.

Put the oil in a pan and add the onion. Cook until soft. Add the remaining fresh vegetables and cook while stirring over high heat for a few minutes.

Pour boiling water over the frozen vegetables and drain them. Combine all the vegetables with the cooked rice.

Sprinkle with the parsley and serve in a pretty dish.

Fried rice

Fried rice can be served as a meal in itself or as an accompaniment to a Chinese meal or other main course. It's quick to prepare if you have some left over cooked rice. The rice should be very dry and fluffy. If you are catering for non-vegetarians, you could include some cooked prawns and pork.

Serves 2 as a main course, 4 as an accompaniment

3 tblsp olive oil

2 eggs

1½ tblsp tamari soy sauce

1 small red onion or plain onion or four spring onions (green onions), chopped

1 small red bell pepper, seeded and cut into small dice

1 small green bell pepper, seeded and cut into small dice

1 fist frozen peas

1 fist frozen corn

4 cups of very dry cooked rice (brown or white)

Garnish

chopped parsley or coriander (cilantro)

Heat a third of the oil in a pan or wok. Beat the eggs with a little of the tamari soy sauce. Then cook them as you would a plain omelette. Remove the cooked egg from the pan, cut it into small pieces and keep hot.

Put half the remainder of the oil in the pan and stir-fry the onion and peppers. Pour some boiling water over the peas and corn to remove the frost, drain them and add them to the pan. Stir fry for about a minute. Remove the vegetables from the pan and keep them hot.

Heat the rest of the oil in the pan and add the cooked rice. Stir-fry the rice until the grains are coated in oil. Add the vegetables, the egg and the remainder of the tamari soy sauce and mix well. Garnish with parsley or coriander (cilantro).

Polenta

Coarse corn meal or polenta comes in two varieties—the ordinary kind which requires 30 minutes cooking while stirring and the precooked kind which takes 1 minute. As life is too short to spend 30 minutes stirring polenta over a hot stove, I recommend that you use the instant variety! The taste is the same—very bland. Flavour the cooked polenta by adding:

- a knob/1 tablespoon of butter;
- some grated cheese—parmesan or a strong blue are very good;
- a crushed garlic clove sautéed in a knob/1 tablespoon of butter;
- some freshly chopped herbs (oregano is good)
- herbs and a hint of chilli or herbs and garlic
- a mixture of cheese, herbs and garlic.

You could also transfer the polenta to an oiled mould or baking tin and allow it to stand and cool for about 1 hour. Then slice it and fry it in a mixture of butter and olive oil or brush it with melted butter and grill (broil) it.

You can freeze the polenta slices.

Plain boiled millet

Serves 4

8 oz/200 g millet

1¼ pints/625 ml/generous 3 cups water

pinch salt

Place the dry millet in a saucepan and roast it over medium heat, tossing it frequently to ensure that it does not burn. When the millet begins to produce a toasty smell, pour the measured cold water over it, being careful not to get splashed. Add salt. Cover and bring to the boil.

Turn down the heat and allow to simmer very, very slowly until all the water is absorbed. This will take about 20 minutes. Turn off the heat and leave to stand in a warm place for about 10 minutes before serving. The millet should be fluffy, nutty and dry.

Millet tabouleh

The appearance and texture of cooked millet is quite similar to bulgar wheat so this is my gluten-free, wheat-free version of the well-known Middle Eastern dish.
Serves 4

6–7 oz/150–175 g millet

a large handful of parsley, washed and dried

finely chopped mint (one third of the amount of parsley)

juice of 1 lemon

a dash of olive oil

salt

freshly ground black pepper

2 fists frozen peas, cooked

Garnish

2 tomatoes, sliced

Cook the millet. Allow it to cool then add the rest of the ingredients. Garnish with the tomato.

Millet & roasted vegetables

This dish can be served hot, warm or cold. Use any surplus for the lunch box or a salad. The millet is cooked and to it is added roasted Mediterranean vegetables. It can be eaten with or without vinaigrette dressing.

Serves 4 (or 2 as a main course)

4 oz/100 g millet

1 small courgette (zucchini), cut into bite size chunks

1 small aubergine (eggplant), cut into bite size chunks

1 small red bell pepper, or ½ red and ½ green bell pepper, seeds removed

1 onion, cut into leaves

a little olive oil

salt

freshly ground black pepper

a sprig of rosemary (optional)

4 cloves garlic, skin on

4 pieces of semi-sundried tomatoes (optional)

Garnish

a few torn basil leaves

Cook the millet as before. Preheat the oven to 200°C/400°F/Gas 6.

Place the prepared vegetables, the rosemary and the garlic cloves in a roasting tin. Drizzle with a little olive oil and coat the vegetables and herbs with it using your hands. Place the roasting tin in the preheated oven and roast the vegetables until they are soft and slightly charred. This will take about 30 minutes.

Remove the garlic pulp from the skins. Mix the vegetables, the garlic pulp, the semi-sundried tomatoes and the cooked millet together. Decorate with the torn basil leaves and serve.

Variation: Brown rice and vegetable salad

Cook as for the previous recipe but use brown rice instead of millet.

Vegetables

When fresh vegetables are cooked with a little care and creativity, they are really appetising and delicious. Cutting vegetables in different ways adds interest. Root vegetables such as turnips, carrots and parsnips can be cut into batons all the same length, or into large or very small dice like dolly mixtures or into very thin strips called julienne strips. Cut on the slant, vegetables are perfect for Chinese cookery.

Vegetables should be as fresh as possible and should be steamed rather than boiled, to preserve their vitamin content. Use the cooking water from boiled vegetables in soup, stock or gravy to recover the lost vitamins and minerals. You can also grill (broil) or roast vegetables. Like meat or fish, vegetables can be marinated in variously flavoured dressings or oils before grilling (broiling) or roasting.

Red cabbage with apple juice

Red cabbage is always a very colourful addition to a meal. Here I use apple juice instead of the usual vinegar which some do not like. (You could also add a splash of wine.)

Serves 4

1 dstsp olive oil

8 oz/250 g red cabbage (about ¼ large cabbage), shredded

1 red or plain onion, peeled and chopped

5–6 whole cloves

1 small cooking apple, peeled and chopped

¾ cup apple juice *or* wine

Heat the oil in a heavy-based saucepan with a tight-fitting lid. Add the cabbage and onion, stir and put the lid on. Reduce to a very low heat and allow the vegetables to sweat for about 15 minutes.

Add the rest of the ingredients and bring to the boil. Reduce the heat and re-place the lid. Allow it to stew for about 20 minutes but watch that it does not burn.

Carrots with ginger

If you do not want to use butter, simply add the grated ginger directly to the carrots.

Serves 4

a knob/1 tsp of butter

1 inch/2 cm piece root ginger, peeled and grated

6 large carrots, peeled, chopped and steamed

Melt the butter in a saucepan and add the grated ginger. Stir over a low heat then add the carrots and toss them in the gingered butter.

Cauliflower Chinese style

Serves 4

1 cauliflower

1 dstsp olive oil

1 tsp sugar

1 cup boiling water

Wash the cauliflower and break it into small florets. Heat the oil in a saucepan and when it is very hot, add the cauliflower and stir-fry until it begins to get brown around the edges.

Dissolve the sugar in the water. Now very carefully add the sweetened water to the cauliflower in the saucepan. It will bubble up furiously. Put the lid on and turn down the heat. The cauliflower will finish cooking in 1–2 minutes depending on the size of the florets. It should be *al dente* rather than soft.

Broccoli Chinese style

Cook as for cauliflower Chinese style, using broccoli instead of cauliflower and adding some chopped ginger to the oil when the broccoli is almost ready to have the water added.

Cooked cucumber

This is delicious with fish, particularly salmon, and is prepared in a jiffy.

Serves 4

1 peeled cucumber, cut into ½ inch/1 cm dice

a knob/2 tsp of butter

1 tblsp chopped fresh mint

salt

freshly ground black pepper

Blanch the cucumber in boiling water for 1 minute. Drain and refresh in cold water. Drain again. Melt the butter in a saucepan and sauté the cucumber over gentle heat for 1–2 minutes. Add the chopped mint and season with salt and pepper.

French beans with garlic butter

French or green beans really need to be steamed until they are quite limp. Then their full flavour comes out. They also taste good with tomato sauce (see page 150).
Serves 4

8 oz/250 g French or green beans
knob/1 tsp butter

1 garlic clove, peeled and crushed

Cook the beans by steaming. Mix together the butter and garlic. Heat the butter and garlic and toss the cooked beans in the garlic butter.

Variation

Substitute Brussels sprouts for the beans in the previous recipe.

Cabbage and bacon

This is a delicious way to serve cabbage.
Serves 4

a little olive oil
1 small onion, peeled and chopped

4 bacon rashers (slices), chopped
1 small head of cabbage, washed and shredded

Heat the oil in a saucepan over medium heat. Add the onion and bacon and fry for 2–3 minutes. Add the cabbage, being careful of the splashes of hot oil. Stir well for 2–3 minutes. Place a cover on the saucepan. Reduce the heat. Cover and leave the cabbage to sweat gently for another 2–3 minutes.

Puy (French green) lentils

This is a very tasty dish to accompany meat or fish or any vegetarian dish. It is a very good vegan dish, served with brown rice and an interesting salad. Lentils cooked in this way can be used very successfully to replace the lamb in a moussaka.
Serves 4

4 oz/100 g puy (French green) lentils

2 red onions, peeled and chopped

2 ripe tomatoes, chopped

2 cloves of garlic, peeled and crushed

1 dstsp olive oil

salt

freshly ground black pepper

Garnish
lots of chopped parsley

Rinse the lentils in cold water. Put them in a saucepan, cover with water and cook until almost done—soft but not mushy. They will take 20–25 minutes. Drain, then add the onions, tomatoes and garlic. Add a little boiling water, just enough to cook the added vegetables. Add the olive oil. Cook with the lid on the saucepan until the vegetables and lentils are cooked. Remove the lid and boil off any excess water. Season with salt and pepper. Garnish with the parsley.

Creamed mushrooms

Serves 4

1 oz/25 g/¼ stick/2 tblsp butter

1 lb/400 g mushrooms, cleaned and
    sliced

1 clove fresh garlic, peeled and
    crushed (optional)

¾ oz/15 g cornflour or maize meal or
    brown rice flour

½ pint/250 ml/1¼ cup milk

salt

freshly ground black pepper

Garnish
chopped fresh parsley

Melt the butter and fry the mushrooms and garlic. Whisk the cornflour into the milk, blend well and add to the cooked mushrooms. Bring to the boil, stirring all the time. Season lightly. Garnish with lots of parsley.

Salads

Let your creativity come to the fore when making salads! Always source the freshest possible ingredients. Starting with greens, you can choose from lettuce of all textures and colours—Chinese leaves or pak choi, spinach, chicory, watercress, rocket (arugula) and fresh herbs. Also include cress and mustard.

Make use of any fresh fruit in season. The juice of fruits can be used as low calorie dressings. Choose from dried fruits, too, such as sultanas (golden raisins), raisins, apricots and prunes.

Though many vegetables can be used raw in salads, such as carrots and celeriac which can be grated, others need to be blanched or cooked. Sprouted seeds should always be blanched as they tend to harbour moulds. Broccoli and cauliflower are good winter salad ingredients—they should be blanched as it makes them more digestible and palatable. To blanch a vegetable, plunge it into boiling water. Bring the water back to the boil and boil it for one minute. Strain through a colander or sieve. Then immediately plunge the vegetable into very cold water to stop the cooking.

Vegetables such as aubergine (eggplant) and courgette (zucchini)are best roasted before including in a salad. Mushrooms should be cooked as should French (green) beans or runner beans. Beetroot (beet) is worth using for its colour alone. Wash it and leave the root and about 2 in/5 cm of the stalks attached (otherwise it will bleed on boiling). Boil it until it is tender. The older and bigger the root the longer it will take. When cooked allow it to cool and remove the stalks, root and skin. It combines very well with the taste and crunchiness of apples or celery.

Remember to include nuts such as almonds, Brazil nuts, walnuts, cashews, peanuts, pine nuts, pecans, and hazelnuts and seeds such as sesame seeds, pumpkin seeds and sunflower seeds. These add a bit of crunch and can be toasted in a dry saucepan over medium heat for extra flavour.

Cooked pulses such as red kidney beans, black eye beans, flageolet beans, haricot beans, chickpeas, garden peas and many more provide protein and very valuable soluble and insoluble fibre. They taste very good in combination with fruits.

Add carbohydrate to your salad by choosing from boiled brown rice, boiled millet, wheat-/gluten-free pasta and boiled or roast potatoes.

For added interest and a Mediterranean flavour don't forget olives, semi-sundried tomatoes and artichoke hearts. Choose from the dressings on pages 127–132 or make up your own recipes.

Tossed mixed summer salad

·

Make a full meal of this salad by adding any of the following: cubes of cheese, cubes of marinated and fried tofu, chopped crisply grilled (broiled) bacon, a hard boiled egg cut into quarters, cooked beans, cold meat or a little poached salmon.

organic lettuce of any kind, washed, at
   least 5 big leaves per person
basil leaves, washed
fennel fronds, washed
parsley, roughly chopped
1 carrot, peeled
avocado slices
1 red or green bell pepper, seeded and
   sliced
peach or nectarine slices
strawberries

cherry tomatoes
red onion rings
chive leaves
cucumber slices
cold potato cubes or cold wheat-/
   gluten-free pasta
olives
semi-sundried tomatoes (optional)
toasted sesame seeds or sunflower
   seeds or pumpkin seeds

Tear the lettuce and basil leaves and mix them with the parsley. Pile these leaves high on the plates. Shave the carrot with an apple peeler into long thin strips. Place all the ingredients except the seeds, fennel and strawberries decoratively on the plate. Drape the fennel fronds over the salad, scatter some toasted sesame or sunflower seeds on top and finish with the strawberries. Serve with a dressing of your choice.

Red rice and minted pea salad

Red rice looks very attractive in a salad.

Serves 1

1–2 oz/25–50 g red rice per person	a squeeze of lemon juice or basic
a fist of frozen peas per person	French dressing
fresh mint, chopped	salt
	freshly ground black pepper

Cook the rice as you would brown rice. Cook the frozen peas, then drain them and add to the cooked rice with some mint and a squeeze of lemon juice or enough dressing to moisten.

Season with salt and pepper and mix all the ingredients together for a very interesting and colourful salad.

Chickpea salad

For this salad, it is best to use cooked dried chickpeas. However, if you are in a hurry use the canned ones, preferably those without added salt or sugar. This is a complete meal for anyone on a vegan diet if served with brown rice and a side salad. It is also very handy for the lunch box.

Serves 4

1 dstsp olive oil

1 onion, peeled and chopped

1 tsp ground cumin

1 tsp ground coriander

1 tsp wheat-/gluten-free curry powder

12 oz/300 g cooked chickpeas

1 banana, peeled and chopped

1 kiwi fruit, peeled and chopped

mayonnaise

salt

freshly ground black pepper

Heat the oil in a pan and fry the onion until it is soft but not coloured. Mix the spices with a little water to form a paste and add this paste to the onion. Fry for a minute or so to cook the spices. Remove from the heat and allow to cool. Add in the chickpeas, the banana and kiwi fruit. When completely cold mix in a little mayonnaise and season with salt and pepper if required.

Cucumber, melon and mint salad

Use about equal quantities of melon and cucumber in this recipe, enough for the number of servings.

Serves 4

½ cucumber

¼ melon

mint, chopped

a squeeze of lemon (optional)

Peel the cucumber and cut it into dice. Cut the melon. Remove the seeds. Cut the flesh into dice and mix it with the cucumber. Mix in some chopped fresh mint and the lemon juice if using.

Mushroom salad

Cooking mushrooms before using them in a salad makes them both tastier and safer.

Serves 4

1 lb/400 g mushrooms

1 dstsp olive oil

1 tblsp mayonnaise

1 tblsp natural (plain) yogurt

a squeeze of lemon juice (optional)

salt

freshly ground black pepper

Wash the mushrooms and cut them into quarters. Place the oil in a saucepan over medium heat and when hot add the mushrooms. Cook the mushrooms in the oil for a few minutes until they are soft. Remove them from the heat when cooked and allow them to get quite cold before adding the mayonnaise, yogurt, lemon juice, salt and pepper.

Coleslaw with horseradish

I am not going to give you quantities here as most people will have made coleslaw before. It is a good way of using up homemade horseradish sauce if you have it left over.

grated cabbage

grated carrot

1 portion mayonnaise

1 portion natural (plain) yogurt

grated horseradish or homemade horseradish sauce

salt

freshly ground black pepper

Make the coleslaw using equal quantities of yogurt and mayonnaise. Then add the horseradish or sauce to taste. If you use the sauce, you could omit the mayonnaise. Season, if necessary, with salt and pepper.

Potato and dill or mint salad

Serves 4

1 lb/500 g potatoes, peeled and
   boiled

1 tblsp natural (plain) yogurt

1 tblsp mayonnaise

lots of chopped fresh dill or mint

salt

freshly ground black pepper

Dice the potatoes and mix them with the yogurt, mayonnaise and dill or mint. Season with salt and pepper.

Curried banana salad

This is ideal served with tandoori chicken.

Serves 4

4 small bananas

wheat-/gluten-free curry paste

enough mayonnaise and/or natural
   (plain) yogurt to bind

Peel and chop the bananas.

Combine the yogurt, mayonnaise and curry paste and mix into the chopped bananas.

Dressings

Dressings are made quickly and easily in a liquidiser or food processor. If you haven't got either, just beat the ingredients together with a balloon whisk and add the chopped herbs if using.

You can flavour your dressing with almost any herb of your choice: parsley, thyme, oregano, basil, chives, summer savoury, rosemary, dill, fennel etc. Be sure to choose mustard which is wheat-/gluten-free.

Apple juice and mustard act as emulsifiers in dressings. These can produce a very thick mayonnaise-like dressing when you use a blender or food processor. If that happens simply thin out the dressing with a little more apple juice, lemon juice or vinegar.

Any left over dressing will keep for a few days in the refrigerator.

Basic French dressing

6 fl oz/150ml/¾ cup olive oil
2 fl oz/50ml/4 tblsp white wine vinegar *or* lemon juice
1 tsp mustard

1 tsp sugar *or* honey *or* apple juice
salt
freshly ground black pepper

Whizz all the ingredients in a food processor or liquidiser.

Variations
Add some chopped herbs to the mix before blending.
Add 1 peeled and smashed clove of garlic to the blended mix. Leave the garlic for an hour or two and remove before serving.

Balsamic dressing

Use the best quality balsamic vinegar you can afford.

6 fl oz/150 ml/¾ cup olive oil
2 fl oz/50 ml/4 tblsp balsamic vinegar

salt
freshly ground black pepper

Whizz all the ingredients in a food processor or liquidiser.

Balsamic dressing with herbs & tamari soy sauce

6 fl oz/150 ml/¾ cup olive oil
2 fl oz/50 ml/4 tblsp balsamic vinegar
fresh herbs
1 tblsp tamari soy sauce

1 tsp honey or apple juice concentrate
1 clove garlic, peeled and smashed
salt
freshly ground black pepper

Whizz all the ingredients, except the garlic, in a food processor or liquidiser. Add the garlic for an hour or two and remove it before serving.

Oriental dressing

This is very good with blanched bean sprouts.

1 in/2 cm piece of ginger

3 fl oz/75 ml/6 tblsp olive oil

1 fl oz/75 ml/6 tblsp toasted sesame
oil

a squeeze of lemon or lime juice

2 cloves garlic, peeled

2 tblsp tamari soy sauce

Fry the ginger gently in the olive oil for a minute or so then whizz all the ingredients in a food processor or liquidiser.

Red bell pepper vinaigrette

6 fl oz/150ml/¾ cup olive oil

2 fl oz/50ml/4 tblsp wine vinegar or
balsamic vinegar or lemon juice

1 red bell pepper, roasted, cooled,
peeled and deseeded

salt

freshly ground black pepper

Whizz all the ingredients in a food processor or liquidiser.

Semi-sundried tomato vinaigrette

2 fl oz/50ml/4 tblsp balsamic vinegar
or wine vinegar or lemon juice

a few basil leaves

4–6 pieces of semi-sundried tomatoes

oil from the tomatoes and olive oil to
make up 6 fl oz/150ml/¾ cup

salt

freshly ground black pepper

Whizz all the ingredients in a food processor or liquidiser.

Orange and coriander (cilantro) dressing

This dressing is low in calories. It is good with carrots.

orange juice

chopped coriander (cilantro)

salt

freshly ground black pepper.

Whizz all the ingredients in a food processor or liquidiser.

Lemon dressing

This dressing is low in calories.

lemon juice

apple juice to sweeten

herbs of choice

salt

freshly ground black pepper.

Whizz all the ingredients in a food processor or liquidiser.

Fennel or dill dressing

Ideal for fish, salads or vegetables this is excellent with hot salmon. If you don't use mayonnaise it is low in calories.

1 small tub organic natural (plain) yogurt or half mayonnaise, half yogurt

1 tblsp chopped fennel *or* dill

1 dstsp lemon juice

1 tsp mustard

salt

freshly ground black pepper.

Whizz all the ingredients in a food processor or liquidiser.

Half fat crème fraîche dressing

This is good on salads and baked potatoes.

½ tub half-fat crème fraîche

½ tub organic natural (plain) yogurt

1 tblsp chopped parsley

1 clove garlic, peeled and smashed

1 tsp salt

freshly ground black pepper

Whizz all the ingredients, except the garlic, in a food processor or liquidiser. Add the garlic and allow the mixture to stand for a few hours and then remove the garlic before serving.

Half and half herb dressing

½ small tub of organic yogurt

½ small tub mayonnaise

1 tblsp herb or herbs of choice

lemon juice to taste

salt

freshly ground black pepper.

Whizz all the ingredients in a food processor or liquidiser.

Semi-sundried tomato dressing

This is very good on vegetables, salads and seafood.

1 small tub organic natural (plain)
  yogurt

4–5 pieces sundried tomatoes and any
  oil adhering to them

salt

freshly ground black pepper

Whizz all the ingredients in a food processor or liquidiser.

Red bell pepper dressing

Low in calories, this is very good on vegetables and salads.

1 small tub organic natural (plain) yogurt

½ red bell pepper, roasted, cooled peeled and deseeded

salt

freshly ground black pepper

Whizz all the ingredients in a food processor or liquidiser.

Lunch box ideas

It isn't always easy to have bread for lunch if you are on a wheat-/gluten-free diet so the following ideas may help you in making up lunches without bread. Use your imagination to create all sorts of different and appealing combinations.

Rice with fish and a dill dressing

This meal can be made with tuna, tinned salmon, sardines or cold, poached, fresh salmon or cod. Tinned fish is very heavily salted so do not add further salt. Brown rice would be preferable to white because of its nutritional value but white Basmati rice cooks very quickly in an emergency. You can use any leftover cooked vegetables such as peas, maize, green beans or carrots.

Serves 1

1 small cup cooked brown or Basmati rice

¼ red bell pepper, chopped

½ stick celery, chopped

cooked vegetables (optional)

fennel or dill dressing (see page 130)

chopped parsley

1 small can of tuna or sardines, drained *or* 2 oz/50 g cooked fresh salmon or cod

3–4 lettuce leaves

1 tomato

6–8 slices of cucumber

Mix all the ingredients together except the lettuce, tomato and cucumber. Place this made up salad in a lunch box with the lettuce, tomato and cucumber and any other salad ingredients of your choice alongside.

Seafood cocktail

Serves 1

3–4 leaves lettuce, shredded

1 small cup cooked rice

3–4 oz/75–100 g cooked cold fish (salmon, cod, hake)

semi-sundried tomato dressing (see page 131)

Shred the lettuce and place it in the lunch box. Place the rice on top and place the fish on top of the rice. Spoon the dressing over.

Add to the lunchbox any of the following: tomato, cucumber, bell pepper, avocado, coleslaw or any other salad ingredient or made up salad of your choice.

Curried rice or pasta with chicken

If you have some leftover roast chicken here is a tasty idea for the lunch box.

Serves 1

2½ oz/60 g wheat-/gluten-free pasta
shapes or 1 small cup cooked rice

1 tblsp sultanas (golden raisins) or
raisins, washed and dried

3–4 oz/75–100 g cold cooked chicken

½ medium red onion or 4 scallions,
finely chopped

½ eating apple, finely chopped

1 stick celery, washed and chopped

2 tsp wheat-/gluten- free curry paste

2 dstsp natural (plain) yogurt

1 dstsp mayonnaise

salad ingredients of your choice

Cook the pasta according to packet instructions. Allow to cool. Mix all the ingredients together. Pile the mixture into a lunch box. To one side place lettuce leaves, tomato, grated carrot, cucumber, chopped celery, or any salad ingredients you have to hand.

Pasta with bacon and leek

Serves 1

2 smoky bacon rashers (slices)

1 very small onion, peeled and sliced

1 clove garlic (optional)

2 inch/5 cm piece of leek, trimmed and
   sliced

1 tsp olive oil

2½ oz/60 g rice pasta

1 oz/25 g frozen peas

a sprinkling of grated cheese

Grill (broil) the bacon rashers (slices). Fry the onion and leek and crushed garlic (if using) in the oil. Turn the heat down to prevent burning and cook until the vegetables are soft. Remove from the heat and allow the mixture to cool. Meanwhile cook the pasta according to the packet instructions. Cook and strain the peas. Combine the rice pasta, peas, bacon and vegetable mixture. Allow to cool completely. If you wish, add a little dressing of your choice, mayonnaise or yogurt. Pile the bacon and leek pasta into a lunch box. Sprinkle with grated cheese. Include in the box any other salad ingredient of your choice e.g. tomato, red bell pepper, corn, celery, carrot, cucumber, avocado, lettuce, herbs etc.

Greek salad

Serves 1

2½ oz/60 g uncooked wheat-/gluten-
   free pasta or a portion of cooked
   potatoes or cooked rice

French dressing with herbs (see page
   128)

2 oz/50 g feta cheese

3–4 large lettuce leaves

1 tomato

4 slices cucumber

¼ red bell pepper

2 or 3 kalamata olives

Boil the pasta and allow it to cool. Moisten the pasta (or potatoes or rice) with the dressing. Place the pasta on the bottom of the lunch box. Place the feta on top. Layer the lettuce, tomato, cucumber and red bell pepper on top of the feta. Finish by decorating with the olives. Toss the whole lot before eating.

Bacon and blue cheese salad

Serves 1

4 lettuce leaves

2 cold roast potatoes

1 oz/25 g blue cheese

2 crisply fried bacon rashers (slices) cut into pieces

4 cherry tomatoes

a few slices of cucumber

a few slices of red bell pepper

mayonnaise

Place the lettuce leaves in the bottom of the lunch box. Put the potatoes on top of the lettuce. Crumble the cheese on top. Scatter the bacon pieces over. Finish with the cherry tomatoes and the slices of cucumber and pepper. Place a little mayonnaise on the side if liked.

Salad Niçoise

This is a good recipe for using up left over green beans and cooked potatoes.

Serves 2

2 portions cooked potato, peeled and diced

1 tsp mayonnaise

1 tblsp natural (plain) yogurt

1 tblsp chopped chives

1 tblsp chopped parsley

salt

freshly ground black pepper

1 small tin tuna fish

4 tblsp cooked green beans

6 lettuce leaves

2 tomatoes

10 slices cucumber

4 olives (optional)

1 hard boiled egg, cut in 4 lengthwise

Add to the potatoes some mayonnaise and natural (plain) yogurt, chives, parsley, salt and pepper. (Alternatively use hot peeled potatoes and dress with a French dressing. Allow to cool before adding to the lunch box.) Put the potato salad into the bottom of the lunch box. On top of it place the tuna fish, then the rest of the ingredients, decorating with the olives and the hard-boiled egg.

Oriental vegan salad

Noodles are used here for convenience. If you have time cook brown rice and use it instead of the noodles.

Serves 2

1 cup bean sprouts

1½ cups cooked rice *or* cooked rice
   noodles

1 small tin red kidney beans, drained

2 tblsp fresh green coriander (cilantro),
   chopped

Oriental dressing (see page 129).

2 dstsp crushed roasted sesame seeds

Trim the stringy roots from the bean sprouts. Plunge them into boiling water. Boil for 1 minute. Rinse them under cold water. Drain. Mix all the ingredients except the sesame seeds. Dress with oriental dressing and place in a lunch box. Garnish with the sesame seeds.

Marinated tofu salad

Tofu is an excellent food, particularly for menopausal women, but make sure to get the organic kind. On its own it is very bland but marinating lends it flavour.

Serves 2

1 packet organic tofu

1 tblsp olive oil

1 tsp chilli oil or a pinch of hot chilli
   powder

2 cloves garlic, peeled and crushed

1 tbsp tamari soy sauce

lemon juice

coriander (cilantro), chopped

salad ingredients of your choice

cooked rice or noodles

Drain the tofu and dry it with kitchen paper. Cut it into cubes. Mix the oils (or the olive oil and chilli powder), garlic, tamari soy sauce, lemon juice and coriander (cilantro) in a bowl. Place the tofu in this mixture and leave it to stand for an hour if you have time. Then empty the mixture into a hot frying pan (skillet). Stir fry until it is heated through. When cold, place it in the lunch box with lots of salad and brown rice or rice noodles.

Asparagus wrap

Wraps are generally made from Mexican flour tortillas. For those who cannot have wheat, pancakes made with wheat-/gluten-free flour are just as good. With one of the fillings suggested below, and a side salad, wraps make excellent lunchtime meals.

Pancake wraps

Make the pancakes according to the filled tortillas recipe (see page 41).
This quantity will make four wraps in an 11 inch/28 cm pan. When the pancake is cold, fill with the desired filling, tucking in both ends before rolling up. Place in the lunch box with the salad of your choice.

Asparagus filling

¼ oz/5 g freshly grated parmesan
4 oz/100 g small tender asparagus spears
a drizzle of basil oil or pesto

Steam the asparagus until tender. This will only take about 2 minutes. Allow to cool. Divide the asparagus between the pancakes and sprinkle the parmesan over the asparagus. Drizzle with basil oil or pesto. Roll up the pancakes.

More fillings for wraps

♦ Grated cheddar cheese with lettuce.
♦ Mashed hard boiled egg, mayonnaise and cress, seasoned.
♦ Poached salmon with mayonnaise, lemon juice, cucumber and lettuce.
♦ Roasted peppers and goats' cheese.
♦ Cottage cheese, chives and corn.
♦ Wedge of cold Spanish omelette with salad.
♦ Cold cashew burger and salad.
♦ Red rice and minted pea salad with tossed greens.
♦ Chickpea salad with cooked brown rice or millet and a green salad.

- ◆ Puy (French green) lentils with brown rice or millet and salad.
- ◆ Tossed mixed salad.
- ◆ Millet and roast vegetable salad.
- ◆ Millet tabouleh.

Tuna pasta salad

Serves 1

2½ oz/60 g wheat/gluten-free pasta per person

1 small tin tuna, drained

1 tblsp cooked sweet corn

¼ red bell pepper

semi-sundried tomato dressing (see page 129)

chopped chives

Cook the pasta. Drain and allow to cool. Mix all the ingredients together. Place in the lunchbox and accompany with tomatoes, cucumber, lettuce or other salad ingredients.

Open sandwiches

Here are a few simple ideas for producing tasty, eye-catching meals in double quick time. All of the sandwiches are made with special bread. Garnish each with a side salad for a very satisfying and colourful dish. If you do not have special bread, then simply make a potato pancake as described on page 42 and top with the same toppings.

Baked tomato, goats' cheese and pine nuts

Serves 2

2 large tomatoes or 4 medium tomatoes	slices of goats' cheese
olive oil	pesto sauce
2 slices special bread (see page 185)	pine nuts, toasted

Cut the tomatoes in two across their equators. Drizzle with olive oil and bake in the oven until soft. Alternatively and for speed, fry them in a little butter and olive oil until soft. Place the tomatoes on the bread. Top with slices of goats' cheese and flash under the grill (broiler). Drizzle with pesto sauce and garnish with a few toasted pine nuts. If you do not have pesto handy, use a few torn fresh basil leaves instead. (To toast pine nuts, put them in a dry saucepan over medium heat and watch them all the time while stirring carefully. Remove them from the saucepan when they are toasted lightly).

Grilled (broiled) Mediterranean vegetables with mozzarella and pesto

In this recipe I use a ridged grill pan to fry the vegetables so that they have a striped appearance. Alternatively use an ordinary frying pan (skillet) or roast the vegetables in the oven. The latter will take a bit longer.

Serves 4

olive oil	4 slices special bread
1 aubergine (eggplant), sliced	freshly ground black pepper
2 small courgettes (zucchini), sliced on the diagonal	6 oz/150 g mozzarella or other cheese of your choice
4 tomatoes, halved around the equator	4 tblsp pesto sauce
1 red onion, peeled and quartered	a few basil leaves

Oil the pan and fry the vegetables on the first side so that they are nicely marked with brown ridges especially the aubergine (eggplant) and courgette (zucchini) slices. If you cannot cook them all in one batch, transfer them to the oven to keep hot while you are cooking the rest. Toast the bread and arrange the vegetables neatly on the toast. Sprinkle with freshly ground black pepper. Top with mozzarella or other cheese of your choice and flash under a hot grill (broiler) until the cheese has melted. Sprinkle the pesto over the top and serve garnished with fresh basil leaves.

Steak and horseradish

Serves 1

4 oz/100 g steak

1 small onion, peeled and sliced

1 slice of special bread

1 heaped tsp homemade horseradish
  sauce

1 oz/25 g cheddar cheese, grated

Cut the steak on the slant into slivers. Cook the steak to taste. Fry the onions. Toast the bread. Place the onions on top of the bread. Put the horseradish sauce on top of the onions. Place the steak on top of the horseradish. Place the grated cheddar on top of the steak. Flash under the grill (broiler). Serve with a salad.

Egg with rocket (arugula)

Serves 1

1 hard boiled egg

a little mayonnaise *or* mayonnaise/
  yogurt mixture

salt

freshly ground black pepper

a fist full of washed rocket leaves

1 slice special bread, buttered

chopped chives

Mash the hard-boiled egg and mix with the mayonnaise. Season with pepper and salt. Arrange the rocket leaves on the bread. Spread the egg mixture over. Decorate with chopped chives.

Melting cheese with artichoke hearts

Serves 2

2 slices of special bread (see page 185)

4 oz/100 gmozzarella, grated or sliced

4–5 pieces of artichoke heart

4–5 pieces of semi-sundried tomatoes

parmesan, freshly grated

olives

Top the bread with the mozzarella. Place a few pieces of artichoke heart and of semi-sundried tomatoes on top. Cover with parmesan and flash under the grill. Decorate with a few olives and serve with a crisp side salad

Avocado and brie

Serves 1

slice of special bread (see page 185)

½ avocado., peeled

slices of brie or similar cheese

butter or garlic butrter (optional)

Toast the bread and butter it if desired. Slice and fan out the avocado and placee it on the toast. Cover with slices of cheese and flash under the grill (broiler).

Savoury sauces and stuffings

Sauces can add greatly to the enjoyment of a meal but unfortunately they often include wheat. The recipes in this chapter will enable you to enjoy many of those sauces you wished you could have. With some of them you will be able to adapt many conventional recipes containing sauces to suit your diet.

If you would like to adapt any stuffing recipes containing wheat to your needs, just omit the breadcrumbs and use brown rice or cooked mashed potato instead. Cooked brown rice mimics breadcrumbs very well in stuffings. The recipe for mock goose on page 108 makes a very good potato stuffing.

Meat gravy

There is nothing nicer with a roast than the gravy made from the meat juices. Forget about gravy browning! All you need is suitable flour, liquid, salt and pepper and, of course, the meat juices.

1 onion, peeled and quartered

1 dstsp potato flour or ¾ oz/15 g cornflour *or* brown rice flour *or* ½ oz/ 10g white rice flour

stock or water or vegetable water

salt

freshly ground black pepper

Put the onion into the roasting tin along with the lamb, beef, pork, chicken or turkey. This caramelizes as the meat cooks and browns the gravy.

When the meat is cooked, remove it from the roasting tin. Drain the fat from the roasting tin. Mix the flour with a little cold water. Add liquid to bring the volume up to ½ pint/250 ml/1¼ cups. Use this to deglaze the roasting dish and season with salt and freshly ground black pepper. Bring the gravy to the boil, stirring all the time, and simmer for a few minutes. If the gravy is too thick for your liking, just add a little more liquid. Strain the gravy through a sieve for a smooth texture.

Basic white or béchamel sauce

This quick and easy sauce is the base for a number of other sauces. For extra flavour infuse the milk by adding a bayleaf, an onion ring, a blade of mace and a sprig of thyme, bring to the boil, stand for 30 minutes, then strain.

¾ oz/15 g cornflour/brown rice flour

½ pt/250 ml/1 ¼ cups plain or infused milk

1 oz/25 g/¼ stick/2 tblsp butter

salt

freshly ground black pepper

Place the flour and milk in a saucepan and whisk with a balloon whisk over a low heat. Add the butter and continue to whisk until the sauce comes to the boil.

Lower the heat and cook for about 1 minute, whisking all the time. Season.

Variations

Cheese or Mornay sauce is particularly good with cauliflower or leeks, or as a dressing for wheat-/gluten-free pasta. It is always included as one of the layers in lasagne to give it a creamy texture. Pour it over fish e.g. cod, haddock, hake, whiting or salmon and bake the fish in the oven until cooked. Try with polenta and roast vegetables for a very colourful and sustaining vegetarian dish. Make a vegetable bake by layering steamed vegetables and cheese sauce and finishing with grated cheese.

To make a cheese sauce add 1 oz/25 g grated cheese: Cheddar, Edam, Leicester or Parmesan to a basic white sauce. As some cheeses are very salty, it is a good idea to add the cheese before seasoning as extra salt may not be required.

Parsley sauce is great with bacon and cabbage and is especially good over most cooked vegetables. Parsley is known as a blood purifier and is rich in iron and magnesium. It helps to purify the breath after eating garlic or onions.

To make parsley sauce, just add lots of finely chopped washed parsley to the basic white sauce.

Mustard sauce is very good with fish.

To make mustard sauce, make a white sauce and add some wheat-/gluten-free mustard.

Velouté sauce Follow the recipe for the basic white sauce but use a very flavoursome homemade stock instead of milk. Use chicken stock where the sauce is to be used with chicken, fish stock for fish. If you wish, finish the sauce by adding a little cream.

White wine sauce This sauce is lovely with fish or chicken. Make a velouté sauce as described and add a splash of white wine. Finish it off by adding a little cream. If the sauce is for chicken, make it with chicken stock, if for fish, use fish stock.

Onion sauce

Traditionally, onion sauce is served with lamb or mutton but it is also very nice as a dressing for vegetables, especially turnips.

¾ oz/15 g cornflour/brown rice flour
½ pt/250 ml/¼ cups plain or infused
  milk
1 oz/25 g/¼ stick/2 tblsp butter

2 oz/50 g peeled and finely chopped
  onion
salt
freshly ground black pepper

Mix the cornflour and milk together in a bowl using a balloon whisk. Put the butter into the saucepan and allow it to melt over medium heat. Stir in the onion and cook without colouring until soft, stirring all the time and turning down the heat if necessary. Remove the saucepan from the heat.

Now, using the balloon whisk, give the mixture in the bowl a stir and whisk it into the cooked onion and butter. Season to taste, replace on the heat and bring it to the boil stirring all the time. Cook for 1 minute while continuing to stir.

Mushroom sauce

Mushroom sauce is wonderful with vegetables or fish. It makes a great filling for pancakes, roulade or other savouries when extra mushrooms are added to the basic sauce recipe.

Follow the method for making onion sauce but use 2 oz/50 g finely chopped mushrooms instead of the onion. You could also add 1oz/25 g of finely chopped wild or exotic mushrooms to intensify the flavour.

Horseradish sauce

This sauce is traditionally served with roast beef.

1 oz/25 g fresh horseradish root

¼ pint/125 ml/generous ½ cup cream,
   whipped lightly or natural (plain)
   yogurt

1 tsp wheat-/gluten-free mustard

1 tblsp vinegar

Peel the horseradish root. Then wash and dry it before grating it. Mix all the ingredients together.

Kiwi and coriander (cilantro) sauce

This sauce is delicious with lamb chops, pork, fish, vegetarian burgers, meat burgers, or even mixed in at the end of stir-frying. It gives a sweet-sour flavour.

2 kiwis, peeled

a little lime zest

juice of ½ lime

1 tblsp chopped fresh coriander
   (cilantro)

caster (super fine) sugar or honey

Mash the kiwi with a fork or blend in a food processor or liquidiser. Mix in the lime zest and juice and the chopped coriander (cilantro). Sweeten to taste with sugar or honey.

Tomato sauce

Fresh tomatoes are always best for this sauce but they have to be very ripe. This sauce can be used for lasagne, pizza and anywhere a tomato sauce is required.

6–7 very red, large tomatoes chopped (in winter use canned tomatoes but omit the water)

1 medium onion, peeled and finely chopped

1–2 cloves garlic, peeled and crushed

1 tblsp olive oil

1 tsp of sugar or to taste

1 tsp dried oregano *or* 1 tblsp chopped fresh oregano

½ tsp dried thyme *or* about 1 tsp chopped fresh thyme

salt

freshly ground black pepper

¼ pint/125 ml/½ cup water or stock (omit if using canned tomatoes)

Fry the onion and garlic gently in the oil. Do not let the garlic burn as it will give a bitter taste. Add the chopped tomatoes and herbs. Stir well and lower the heat. Add water or stock. Continue to cook over a very low heat until the tomatoes have cooked to a pulp and the sauce has thickened. Add sugar to taste if the sauce is a bit bitter.

Variation

Omit the onion and at the end of cooking add lots of fresh basil instead of the oregano and thyme.

Pesto sauce

Pesto sauce is very versatile and easy to make. It goes very well with all kinds of cheese but especially goats' cheese. It is also wonderful with roast vegetables, tomato dishes, fresh tomatoes or a salad composé, or tossed into hot wheat-/gluten-free pasta. I tend to put the garlic in it only if I am using it straight away. This sauce can be refrigerated for 2–3 days.

½ oz/10 g basil, washed and dried

4 fl oz/100 ml/generous ½ cup extra virgin olive oil

¾ oz/15 g freshly grated parmesan

½ oz/10 g pine nuts

1 clove garlic, peeled and crushed (optional)

a few twists of black pepper

Place all the ingredients in the food processor and whizz. There should be no need for salt as the cheese is very salty.

Mango salsa

This salsa, which is bursting with colour and flavour, is very simple to make. Serve it with grilled (broiled) meat, chicken, cold meat, fish, cashew burgers, or meat burgers. If there is any left, you could combine it with cooked rice or millet to make a delicious tropical salad.

½ large red bell pepper, finely chopped

½ large red onion, peeled and finely chopped

juice of ½ lime

½ large mango *or* 1 small mango peeled and finely chopped

1 tblsp roughly chopped coriander (cilantro)

Combine all the ingredients in a bowl and stir. Prepare as near to the time of serving as possible.

Red bell pepper sauce

You don't have to use homemade stock in this sauce as a vegetable stock cube works very well. It is a very good sauce with wheat-/gluten-free pasta and with grilled (broiled) chicken or grilled fish. You could also serve it with vegetable burgers or as a dressing for steamed vegetables. If you have time, it is worthwhile peeling the peppers though this is not absolutely necessary. I find the best way to peel them is to brush the whole peppers all over with olive oil and bake them on a baking sheet in a hot oven until the skin is slightly charred and blistered. Then remove them from the oven, cool them under the cold tap, and the skin pulls away easily.

1 lb/500 g red bell peppers, deseeded and peeled

1 tblsp olive oil

1 medium onion, peeled and finely chopped

2 cloves garlic, peeled

2 medium sized ripe tomatoes

1 tsp chopped fresh thyme

¾ pint/400 ml/1¾ cups stock

salt

freshly ground black pepper

Heat the oil in a saucepan. Add the onion and garlic and cook without colouring over slow heat until the onion is soft and translucent, stirring all the time. Add the rest of the ingredients, cover, and continue to cook over slow heat until the peppers are soft. Liquidise in a liquidiser or food processor. Reheat before serving.

Citrus yogurt sauce

This cold sauce can be used with grilled (broiled) fish or meat. It is equally good with vegetarian burgers, salads or vegetables.

1 small carton organic natural (plain)
   yogurt
An equal quantity of half-fat crème
   fraîche
zest and juice of 1 orange

zest of 1 lemon or lime
juice of ½ lemon or enough to make a
   thin sauce
salt
freshly ground black pepper

Mix all the ingredients together.

Dill and lemon sauce

This sauce is especially good with hot or cold poached salmon, and is also an excellent dressing for a potato salad. If you omit the mayonnaise it is virtually fat free. Even with the mayonnaise it is much lower in fat than pure mayonnaise.

1 small tub organic natural (plain)
   yogurt
zest of ¼ lemon
1 tblsp lemon juice
1 tblsp mayonnaise (optional)

1 tsp gluten-free/wheat-free mustard
1 tblsp chopped fresh dill *or* fennel
salt
freshly ground black pepper

Mix all the ingredients together. Garnish with a 'fern' of dill or fennel.

Mayonnaise

The mayonnaise you buy is made with pasteurised egg and provided you are sure it is wheat-/gluten-free, it is safe to use. Homemade mayonnaise is made with raw egg. As with any food containing raw egg, it should not be given to the elderly, the sick or babies. It must be kept refrigerated and eaten within a few days. The eggs should be very fresh for mayonnaise and the oil should be at room temperature and added very slowly—drop by drop at the beginning.

2 fresh free range or organic egg yolks
1 dstsp wine vinegar or lemon juice
¼ tsp wheat-free/gluten-free mustard
salt
freshly ground black pepper

½ pint/250 ml/1¼ cup olive oil and
   unrefined sunflower or safflower oil
   (half and half)

Place the egg yolks, lemon juice or vinegar, mustard, salt and pepper in a liquidiser or food processor and whizz. Very, very slowly add the oil—drop by drop at the beginning, until all the oil is used up. Refrigerate. If the mayonnaise becomes too thick, thin it out with lemon juice, vinegar or hot water.

Apricot and ginger stuffing

This stuffing is particularly delicious with roast pork or pork steak but can be used to stuff any meat or vegetables.

1 oz/25 g/¼ stick/2 tblsp butter
1 large onion, peeled and chopped
1½ inch/4 cm piece root ginger, peeled
   and finely chopped
8 apricots, chopped

zest and juice of 1 orange
8 oz/200 g dry and fluffy cooked
   brown rice
salt
freshly ground black pepper

Heat the butter in a saucepan, add the onion and cook gently. Add the ginger. Cook over a low heat for a minute or two. Add the apricots, the orange zest and juice and the rice. Season with salt and pepper.

Hazelnut stuffing

This stuffing is very good with turkey but is also excellent with game or red meats. It can also be used to stuff vegetables. Omitting the bacon and replacing it with a tablespoon of freshly chopped rosemary or coriander (cilantro) makes a very tasty and nutritious vegetarian stuffing.

4 oz/100 g hazelnuts
1 dstsp olive oil
2 bacon rashers (slices), chopped
1 tblsp each of very finely chopped
   carrot, celery, onion

zest and enough juice of 1 orange to
   moisten the stuffing
6 oz/150 g dry and fluffy cooked
   brown rice
salt (if required)
freshly ground black pepper

Place the nuts in a dry saucepan over moderate heat. Stir them while allowing them to toast. Some of the skins will fall off and the nuts will get nicely toasted in patches. Remove the saucepan from the heat and transfer the hazelnuts to a clean dry tea towel. Rub them in the towel until the skins fall off. It does not matter if some of them remain on. Place the nuts in a food processor and whizz them until they are finely chopped. Heat the oil in a saucepan. Add the bacon rashers (slices) and the vegetables. Cook for a few minutes over moderate heat. Now mix all the ingredients together.

'Let go of how you thought your life should
be and embrace the life that is trying to
work its way into your consciousness.'

Caroline Myss

Desserts and dessert sauces

Rhubarb pudding

This recipe was given to me by my friend, Stephanie. She in turn got it from her mother. I have adapted it to suit the diet. You could vary it with fruits in season.

Serves 4

½ cornflour or rice flour sponge cake
  (see page 187)
4 large sticks of rhubarb, stewed and
  slightly sweetened

zest and juice of 1 orange
a pinch of cinnamon
2 large egg whites
4 oz/100 g unrefined caster (super
  fine) sugar

Put the sponge cake on the bottom of an ovenproof dish. Mix the rhubarb, orange zest and juice, and cinnamon and pour this mixture over the sponge cake. Cover the dish and place it in the oven at 180°C/350°F/Gas 4 until heated through.

Meanwhile, make the meringue. Beat the egg whites until stiff, then beat in the sugar and whisk until stiff peaks are formed.

Remove the dish from the oven. Place the meringue on top of the rhubarb. Replace the dish in the oven and bake until the meringue begins to colour nicely—this will take about 10 minutes.

Chocolate roulade

If you see this on a restaurant menu, don't automatically assume that it is without wheat and/or gluten as there is wheat flour in some recipes. This recipe has no flour of any kind.

Serves 4

4 eggs, separated
4 oz/100 g unrefined caster (super
  fine) sugar

4 oz/100 g dark (semi-sweet) chocolate
1 medium carton of cream
fresh fruit to fill (optional)
icing (confectioner's) sugar

Preheat the oven to 200°C/400°F/Gas 6. Whisk the egg whites until stiff but not dry. Beat the yolks with the sugar. Melt the chocolate in a bowl over hot but not boiling water. Add the chocolate to the yolk mixture, stirring all the time. Fold the egg whites into the yolk mixture.

Gently spread the mixture over a Swiss roll tin lined with baking parchment, greased and dusted with cornflour. Bake it in the oven for 20 minutes. Turn it out onto a wire tray covered with a sheet of baking parchment to cool and roll it up gently.

Unroll it when it is cool. Fill it with whipped cream and fresh fruit (if using) and roll again. It will probably split but don't worry as it will look all the more luscious for it!

Dust the roulade with suitable icing sugar (confectioner's sugar) and serve.

Sweet pastry (pie dough) without egg

This is a delicious short pastry (pie dough). It is lighter than the recipe which follows, which contains an egg. You can use either where a sweet pastry (pie dough) is required.

3 oz/75 g potato flour
3 oz/75 g soya flour
6 oz/150 g rice flour
2 oz / 50 g caster sugar (super fine sugar)

1 oz/25 g linseeds, milled finely in a food processor or liquidiser
6 oz/150 g/1 ½ sticks/¾ cup butter

Sift the flours together into a bowl. Add the sugar and linseeds. Cut the butter into cubes and using the tips of the fingers, rub it into the flour mixture. Add water to bind. More water will be needed than would be required for the same quantity of wheaten pastry (pie dough)—it should be ever so slightly sticky. It will roll quite well immediately.

Sugar pastry or pâte sucrée

This is a rich sweet pastry (pie dough) suitable for mince pies, flans, tartlets, tarts etc. It is important to follow the method given. The addition of the sugar to the egg before the butter allows the granules of sugar to dissolve in the egg giving the pastry a smooth finish. This pastry may be difficult to roll—in that event patch it! No one will know when it is filled.

Makes 2 small flans or 10 tartlets

1½ large eggs or 2 small eggs, beaten

3 oz/75 g unrefined caster (superfine) sugar

½ tsp natural almond essence (extract)

7½ oz/185 g butter

6 oz/150 g brown rice flour

3 oz/75 g soya flour

3 oz/75 g potato flour

1 oz/25 g finely crushed golden linseeds

In a food processor or mixer beat the eggs and sugar and almond essence (extract) together. Add the butter and mix again. Combine the flours and sieve together. Add the flour mixture and the linseeds to the food processor bit by bit. When all the flour is added the food processor should gather the mixture into a ball. At this stage stop the processor. Remove the pastry (pie dough) and use it as desired. It makes wonderful French fruit tartlets or flans.

Flan case

1 quantity sweet or sugar pastry (pie dough)

Pre-heat the oven to 220°C/425°F/Gas 722. Roll out the pastry to the desired thickness. Place over a greased flan tin with a removable base. Trim the edges and tuck down the rim of the pastry.

Alternatively, use a sandwich tin or flan ring. Roll out the pastry so that it is big enough to come up the sides of the tin/ring. Grease the tin/ring. Place the pastry over the tin. Gently press it down into the base. Roll the rolling pin across the top of the tin to trim the pastry.

Now place a sheet of baking parchment over the pastry. Place dried peas or chick-peas on top to weight it down. Bake the flan case until pale golden and firm (it should only take about 15 minutes or less).

Remove the flan case from the oven and cool on a wire rack. Remove the peas carefully together with the parchment paper and allow the flan case to cool in the tin.

If you use a flan tin with a removable base, place the tin upside-down on the wire tray and remove the ring and base.

Banana and orange flan

This is quite a filling dessert so a little goes a long way. You could make the flan case in advance but leave the finishing touches closer to mealtime as the bananas tend to discolour.

Serves 4

3–4 bananas

1 small carton cream, whipped or
    crème fraîche if preferred

grated chocolate

1 flan case (see page 160)

apricot jam

zest and juice of 1 orange

1 dstsp unrefined caster (superfine)
    sugar

Spread some apricot jam over the base of the flan case. Meanwhile mix the orange zest and juice with the sugar. Slice the bananas into the flan case. Sprinkle the orange juice mixture over them. Spread the whipped cream over the top and decorate with grated chocolate.

French fruit tartlets

You can vary the fruit used in the following recipe. Choose from the following: peaches, nectarines, strawberries, gooseberries, raspberries, blackberries, cooked dried apricots. If you wish you can use pastry cream under the fruit in these tartlets.

Makes 12 tartlets

1 quantity of pâte sucrée

apricot jam

1 tsp lemon juice

1 lb/500 g fruit

cream, whipped

toasted almond flakes

Pre-heat the oven to 200°C/400°F/Gas 6. Roll out the pastry (pie dough) (not too thinly) and place it on top of the greased tartlet tins. Gently mould it into the tins with your hands. Now roll the rolling pin over the tartlet tins to cut the pastry. Press the pastry gently against the sides of the tartlet tins with your fingers. Bake the tartlets in the preheated oven. They will take only 10 minutes or less so keep a watchful eye on them. Take them from the oven and allow them to cool in the tins.

Just before using, remove the tartlets very carefully and gently from the tins. Spread a little apricot jam over the bottom of each tartlet. Slice the strawberries and fill each tartlet with the slices. Make some apricot glaze: beat 1 tbsp apricot jam, 1 tbsp water and 1 tsp lemon juice together. Brush the glaze over the fruit. Decorate with the whipped cream and toasted almonds and serve immediately.

Plum compote with crème anglaise

This dessert is very attractive in appearance—the vibrant red of the plums contrasts beautifully with the sauce. You can vary it by using other fruits instead of plums.

Serves 4

¼ pint/125 ml/generous ½ cup water

2 dstsp unrefined caster (superfine) sugar

1 vanilla pod, split and seeds removed

8 plums

crème anglaise (see page 174)

162

Boil the water and sugar to make syrup. Add the vanilla seeds and pod to flavour it. Wash and cut the plums around their equators but leave them whole. Place them in the hot syrup and cook, with the lid on, over gentle heat until they are soft but not mushy.

Remove the pod. Serve the plums on plates with a little of the colourful juice. Pour the crème anglaise around the plums and syrup for a very attractive dessert.

Almond apple crunch

Here I use almond macaroon mixture to make this delicious dessert which has a crunchy topping. The mixture can also be used as a topping for stuffed apples before you bake them.

For the macaroon mixture

2–3 egg whites (depends on size)

4 oz/100 g ground almonds

4 oz/100 g unrefined caster (superfine) sugar

1 oz/25 g maize flour or cornflour

1 oz/25 g brown rice flour

½ tsp natural almond essence (extract)

For the filling

1 large cooking apple, peeled and sliced

Preheat the oven to 180°C/350°F/Gas 4. Lightly whip the egg whites. Mix the dry ingredients together. Add enough of the egg white to the dry mixture to make a soft paste. Add the almond essence (extract) and mix again.

Mark out a 6 in/15 cm circle with a pencil on a piece of baking parchment. Place the disc of paper on a baking tray and grease the surface of the parchment. Now spread half the mixture onto the disc. Place the sliced apple in neat circles on top. Spread the remaining mixture over the apple and bake in the preheated oven. It will take 45 minutes to 1 hour to cook the apples through.

Serve either on its own or with whipped cream or crème anglaise. You could vary this recipe by using some stewed apricots instead of the apple.

Crumble topping with rice bran or millet flakes

Crumbles are some of the easiest and most versatile of dishes for those who are on a wheat- and/or gluten-free diet. When made with rice bran, crumble has a rusk-like flavour, when made with millet flakes it is nice and crunchy. Crumble can be used on any kind of fruit, for example plums, raspberries, pears, apples, rhubarb or mixed fruit. To cut down on cooking time, stew the fruit first in a covered saucepan over low heat using either a little water or a knob (1 tablespoon) of butter melted in the bottom of the saucepan. Omit the sugar from the crumble mixture and you have a crumble topping for a savoury dish.

Serves 4

2 oz/50 g brown rice flour

2 oz/50 g rice bran or millet flakes

2 oz/50 g unrefined caster (superfine) sugar

2 oz/50g/½ stick/¼ cup butter

1 tblsp cold water

Mix the dry ingredients together. Add the butter and rub it into the dry ingredients with the tips of your fingers. Mix in cold water—1 tbsp or enough to form a breadcrumb-like texture.

Rhubarb and ginger crumble

Serves 4

1 lb/450 g rhubarb, cleaned and chopped

2 oz/50 g crystallised ginger, chopped in fine pieces

unrefined caster (super fine sugar) sugar

1 quantity crumble topping

Mix the rhubarb and ginger in a pie dish. Add enough sugar to sweeten. Cover the rhubarb with the crumble topping. Bake in the oven at 200°C/400°F/Gas 6 for about 30 minutes with a lid on. Remove the lid as soon as the rhubarb is cooked (test with a knife) and cook for a further 5 minutes to crisp the top.

Alternatively cook the rhubarb in a saucepan on top of the stove using two tablespoons of water or a knob (1 tablespoon) of butter to prevent the rhubarb from sticking. Transfer the stewed rhubarb to a pie dish and top with the crumble mixture. Bake in the oven until the crumble is crisp.

Serve hot with cream, yogurt or ice cream.

Apple crumble

Serves 4

1 lb/450 g cooking apples

unrefined caster (superfine) sugar

1 quantity crumble topping

Peel, core and slice the apples. Place them in a saucepan with a knob (1 tablespoon) of butter and cook over slow heat until soft. Sweeten to taste, transfer the cooked apple to a pie dish and top with the prepared crumble mixture. Bake at 200°C/400°C/Gas 6 until the crumble is cooked. Serve hot with cream yogurt or ice cream.

Sherry trifle

Serves 4

1 cornflour or rice flour sponge cake
   (see page 187)

homemade strawberry or raspberry jam

sweet sherry

strawberries, raspberries or ripe pears

pastry cream (see page 172)

cream, whipped

Make little sandwiches of the sponge cake and jam. Put these in a layer on the bottom of a pretty glass dish.

Sprinkle the sherry liberally over the sponge cake. Now place a layer of fruit over the cake. Next pour on the cold pastry cream. Finish with a layer of whipped cream and decorate as desired.

Éclairs

Makes about 10 éclairs

For the choux pastry
2 oz/50g/½ stick/¼ butter
¼ pint/125 ml/generous ½ cup water
3 oz/75 g rice flour, sifted
½ tsp wheat-/gluten-free baking powder, sifted

a small pinch of salt
½ oz/10 g ground linseeds
2 large eggs, beaten
To finsh
whipped cream
melted chocolate or coffee water icing

Preheat the oven to 200°C/400°F/Gas 6.

Place the butter and water in a saucepan and bring to the boil. Remove from the heat and add the sifted flour, baking powder, salt and linseeds all in one go. Beat the mixture with a wooden spoon for 1 minute over gentle heat.

Remove the saucepan from the heat and allow the contents to cool slightly.

Now transfer the mixture to a mixing bowl. Using an electric mixer, beat the mixture while adding the beaten eggs a little at a time. Continue to beat until the mixture is smooth and glossy.

Using a dessert spoon, transfer the mixture in spoonfuls onto a non-stick baking tray. Bake in the preheated oven for about 40 minutes or until the outsides are golden and the insides are hollow and dry. Test one after about 30 minutes by opening with a knife. When cooked, remove the eclairs from the oven and place on a wire rack to cool.

When cold, fill with whipped cream and ice with melted chocolate or coffee water icing.

Variations

Fill with crushed raspberries or strawberries and whipped cream and serve with a fruit coulis or chocolate sauce.

For Eskimo puffs: Fill éclairs with ice cream and serve with chocolate sauce.

For profiteroles: Fill éclairs with cream and serve with chocolate sauce.

Carrigeen jelly

Carrigeen moss has long been used as an invalid food and it is particularly soothing for sore throats. My mother often makes carrigeen as a dessert though she does not believe in masking its seaweed taste with vanilla as I do! She often made drinks for us as children by boiling carrigeen in water, straining it and then adding lemon juice and honey. As sea vegetables provide us with lots of protein and are rich in iodine, it is good to have this traditional dessert of carrigeen moss now and again. If you are one of those people whose coeliac condition has given rise to dermatitis herpetiformis, *avoid carrigeen as iodine exacerbates this skin condition.*

Serves 4

1 closed fistful carrigeen moss
1½ pint/750 ml/3¾ cups milk
1 tsp natural vanilla extract (essence) or
    a vanilla pod split open

1 tblsp unrefined caster (superfine)
    sugar

Wash the carrigeen and soak for 10 minutes in a bowl of cold water. Squeeze it out and add it to the milk in a pan together with the vanilla pod if using one. Bring the milk to the boil and simmer gently for about 15 minutes.

Strain the boiled milk through a sieve. Press as much as possible through the sieve.

Add the vanilla essence (extract) at this stage if you are using it. If you are using a vanilla pod, scrape the seeds from the inside and add them to the milk.

Sweeten the milk, transfer it to a bowl and allow it to cool.

Chill in the refrigerator and serve with your choice of fresh fruit, fruit coulis (see page 175) or fruit compote.

Cool krispie ring

This dessert is ideal for children of all ages! Make sure you use a brand of puffed rice that does not contain malt or any of its derivatives. There is a good one available in the health food shops.

Serves 4

4 oz/100 g wheat-/gluten-free chocolate

3 oz/75 g wheat-/gluten-free puffed
rice

softened ice cream to fill the ring

lots of fresh fruit to decorate

grated chocolate to decorate

Heat the chocolate in a basin over hot water. Do not let the water boil. When the chocolate has melted, add the puffed rice and mix thoroughly. Grease a ring tin and fill it with the mixture. Now get a dessertspoon or spatula and press the mixture firmly into the tin so that the krispies are compacted and the top smooth. Place in a cool place until the chocolate is firm.

Now fill a basin with very hot water. Carefully dip the ring tin into the water so that the chocolate in contact with the ring tin melts. (About 20 seconds is suffi-cient.) Dry the outside of the tin. Place a large flat plate over the ring tin and invert the lot. The krispie ring should fall out onto the plate.

When you are ready to serve the dessert, fill the ring with softened ice-cream and decorate with lots of fresh fruit and some grated chocolate.

Fruit condé

Choose any fruit to serve with the condé—strawberries, raspberries, ripe pears, stewed prunes, apricots etc.

Serves 4

1 pint/500 ml/2½ cups milk

3 oz/75 g pudding rice

½ tsp natural vanilla essence (extract) or flavour the milk with the seeds of a vanilla pod

1 dstsp sugar or icing (confectioner's) sugar to taste

6 fl oz/150 ml/¾ cup cream, whipped

fruit to serve

grated chocolate

Bring the milk to the boil. Add the rice and stir. Continue to cook over a low heat stirring from time to time until the rice is cooked. Add the vanilla essence (extract) and the sugar. Allow the rice to cool.

Fold the whipped cream into the rice, reserving some for decoration. Spoon the rice into individual glass dessert dishes and decorate with the fruit of your choice. Top with the reserved whipped cream and sprinkle with grated chocolate if desired.

Plum pudding

Until she got married, my youngest sister, Phil, was my mother's chief assistant when making the plum puddings for Christmas. A whole evening was dedicated to the task. This plum pudding is based on my mother's which I think is one of the best. She made the puddings in bulk, usually about twelve, which she mixed in a huge, blue, plastic dish. My recipe here is sufficient to make just two small, 2 pint/ 1 litre/5 cup puddings or 1 large pudding. Remember to keep up the old tradition of giving everyone a chance to stir the pudding in order to have a wish. I'm not sure if the wishes come true, but it is a great way of getting a little help!

Makes 2 small or 1 large pudding

4 oz/100 g/1 stick/½ cup butter

5 oz/125 g brown rice flour

1½ tsp grated nutmeg

2 oz/25 g millet flake

6 oz/150g unrefined dark brown sugar

8 oz/200 g raisins, washed and dried

8 oz/200 g sultanas (golden raisins), washed and dried

3 oz/75 g dates, stoned and chopped

3 oz/75 g apricots, chopped

4 oz/100 g cherries

1 oz/25 g candied peel, chopped (any excess sugar removed)

zest and juice of 1 lemon

zest and juice of 1 orange

1 medium apple, peeled and grated

2 oz/50 g ground almonds

½ carrot, peeled and grated

2 measures (3 fl oz/75 ml/6 tblsp) dark rum

3 large eggs, beaten

Melt the butter slowly in a saucepan over low heat. Sift the flour and mix all the dry ingredients together.

Mix all the fruits in another bowl and add the lemon and orange zest and juice, the grated apple, the grated carrot and the rum.

Add the dry ingredients, then the beaten eggs and finally the melted butter.

Grease one large or two small bowls and place a piece of greaseproof or parchment paper on the bottom. Fill the bowl or divide the mixture between the two bowls. Do not fill to the top but leave about 1 in/2 cm of the bowl above the mixture.

Put a greased disc of greaseproof or parchment paper directly on top of the mix. Then cover with a double thickness of greaseproof or parchment paper with a pleat in the centre. Secure the greaseproof with cotton twine. Now cover the greaseproof with tinfoil and secure.

Place in a large saucepan on top of a crumpled piece of greaseproof or parchment paper and pour in boiling water until the water comes about two-thirds of the way up the side of the bowl. Cover the saucepan with the lid and bring the water back to the boil. Turn down the heat and simmer until cooked. Make sure that the saucepan does not boil dry by topping it up occasionally with boiling water. The pudding(s) will take at least 3 hours cooking. The more it is cooked the darker it gets.

When cooked remove the lid and replace with fresh greaseproof or parchment paper and tinfoil. Store in a cool dry place. When needed steam in the same way for about 1½ hours.

The pudding can be served with wheat-/gluten-free brandy or rum sauce (see page 175), brandy butter, whipped cream, whipped cream flavoured with brandy or rum or brandy punch.

Pastry cream

This pastry cream is very suitable for filling flan cases or éclairs.

4 egg yolks

4 oz/100 g sugar

1 tsp natural vanilla essence (extract)

1½ oz/35 g cornflour

1 pint/500 ml/2½ cups milk

Mix the egg yolks, the sugar, the vanilla essence (extract) and the cornflour together in a bowl and add a little of the milk. (The cornflour stops the egg yolks from cracking when heated.) Boil the rest of the milk in a saucepan.

Add the boiling milk to the egg yolk mixture, whisking all the time. Now transfer the entire mixture back into the saucepan and, stirring all the time, allow it to come slowly up to boiling point. Cornflour takes very little cooking—about 1 minute will suffice. Now cool the mixture by standing the saucepan in cold water and beating all the time to prevent a skin from forming on the custard.

Orange sauce

A good accompaniment to orange gateau, marmalade cake, meringues etc.

2–3 oranges

¾ oz/15 g cornflour

sugar to taste

2 tblsp Cointreau, or other orange liqueur (optional)

Grate the rind from 1 orange and then juice all the oranges. Blend the cornflour with a little of the orange juice, then stir in the rest of the juice and the rind. Bring the mixture to the boil, stirring all the time. Cook for about 1 minute. Taste and then add sugar if required and cool. If using liqueur stir it in now.

Prune and orange sauce

This sauce is very good with chocolate ice cream.

8 oz/225 g packet of prunes, cooked   zest of 1 orange

juice of 2 oranges   1 tblsp orange liqueur (optional)

Drain the prunes and reserve the cooking liquid. Purée the prunes together with the orange zest and juice and the liqueur. Thin the sauce if necessary by adding some of the cooking liquid.

Quick chocolate sauce

This is convenience chocolate sauce as it can be prepared so easily! Children love it. Give it to them with stewed pears and vanilla ice cream. Use it too for banana split: 1 banana per person, 1 spoon of homemade jam, 1 scoop of ice-cream, chocolate sauce and whipped cream.

3 fl oz/75 ml/6 tblsp milk

3 oz/75 g wheat-/gluten-free dark (semi-sweet) chocolate

Place the milk and chocolate in a heat-proof basin. Place the basin over hot water. Do not allow the water to touch the basin and do not allow the water to come to the boil. Leave it undisturbed until the chocolate is soft. Now whisk the chocolate and milk together.

Strawberry and elderflower sauce

Other fruits such as raspberries, blackcurrants, stewed gooseberries, loganberries, etc. are also good with elderflower cordial.

1 punnet strawberries
3 tblsp elderflower cordial or to taste

Purée the strawberries in a blender or food processor and stir in the elderflower cordial. Serve with ice cream or fresh fruit.

Crème anglaise or pouring egg custard

You could make this with brown rice flour or with cornflour or maizeflour but rice powder gives a lovely glossy appearance to the finished sauce.

1¼ pint/625 ml/3 cups milk
2 egg yolks
½ oz/10 g rice powder (2 rounded dstsp)
(or cornflour or brown rice flour)

1–2 oz/25–50 g unrefined caster (super fine) sugar
1 tsp natural vanilla essence (extract) or the seeds from a vanilla pod

Place three-quarters of the milk in a saucepan and bring to the boil. Mix the egg yolks with the rest of the ingredients and the remainder of the milk in a bowl. Add the boiling milk to the egg mixture, whisking all the time. Pour the custard back into the saucepan and bring it back to the boil while continuing to whisk. Turn the heat down and cook for a few minutes.

Serve with stewed fruit or apple tart or use to decorate a dessert plate either on its own or with fruit coulis. Use the egg whites to make almond macaroons, macaroon-topped baked apples, meringues or pavlova or instead of whole egg to bind such things as burgers or rissoles.

Fruit coulis

You can make fruit coulis from many fruits especially raspberries, mangoes, straw-berries, kiwi, blackcurrants. Some cooks sieve the coulis to give the sauce a smooth appearance but this is unnecessary.

fruit of your choice   icing (confectioner's) sugar to taste

Purée the flesh of the fruit in a food processor or liquidiser and sweeten if neces-sary with the sugar.

Serve fruit coulis with gateau, fresh fruit, ice cream, pavlova or meringues.

Brandy or rum sauce

This is the wheat-/gluten-free version of my favourite accompaniment to Christ-mas pudding. For the smoothest glossiest sauce, use white rice flour or rice powder instead of cornflour. You will need more milk if you are using white rice flour as it has greater thickening powers than cornflour.

¾ oz/15g cornflour
½ pint/250 ml/1¼ cup milk
(or ¾ oz/15g white rice flour
¾ pt/375 ml/1¾ cups milk)

1 oz/25 g/¼ stick/2 tblsp butter
1–2 measures brandy or rum
1 tblsp unrefined caster (super fine)
   sugar

Put the flour and milk into a saucepan and whisk with a wire whisk until the flour is incorporated in the milk.

Add the butter and place over medium heat whisking all the time. When the mixture comes to the boil turn down the heat and simmer while stirring for 1 minute.

Take off the heat and add the brandy (or rum) and sugar. Do not boil again or the brandy will evaporate.

'The use of love makes me feel good, it is an expression of my inner joy.'

Louise L. Hay

Baking

All the flours in the recipes in this book are naturally wheat- and gluten-free. If you cannot tolerate soya flour which is used in some recipes, use gram/chickpea flour instead. Alternatively, replace it with the main flour in the recipe.

Many commercial wheat- and/or gluten-free flours and breads contain additives such as xanthan gum and guar gum. These are used to help bind and rise the bread but can result in a very slimy mouth feel. I searched for a nutritious alternative natural ingredient that would bind and rise the bread. Golden linseeds provided a solution. The linseeds must be either soaked for a few hours or overnight in the liquid used in the recipe, or ground finely and added to the dry ingredients. The presence of an egg or eggs in a recipe will also help the rising of the dough. I have found that one of the most difficult aspects of making wheat-/gluten-free breads is gauging the optimum quantity of liquid to use to get the best results; too much and the bread will have the texture of a crumpet; too little and it will be very close, heavy and dry. All the breads in this book are made from batter rather than dough. The consistency of the batter should be a bit like that for queen cakes. I can only say that practice makes perfect!

When using yeast, the water in the recipe must be at blood heat. To achieve this, mix two parts cold with one part boiling water. All wheat-free and gluten-free breads and scones go stale very quickly. They are best eaten on the day they are made. Use a very sharp serrated knife to slice them. Homemade breads are delicate so handle with care. If you freeze them you will need to freshen them up by either toasting or reheating before use. When making cakes use deep straight-sided baking tins rather than shallow tins with sloping sides and you will get a better result. If your tins are bigger than those I have used, adjust the recipe accordingly.

The first two recipes are for light sponge cakes; the difference between them is that the first is made from cornflour or maize flour, whereas the second is made from brown rice flour. You could also use white rice flour or rice powder which will give more or less the same texture but the brown is the healthier option. Both recipes produce very good sponges, the first one being extremely light and smooth, the second more grainy and satisfying as it has more body. They make great bases for such desserts as sherry trifle, baked Alaska, tiramisu and gateaux of various kinds.

The sandwich cakes which follow the plain sponge cakes are all made with butter. Margarine will give a better rise because it contains emulsifiers. If you use very fresh eggs with the butter you will get a very good result. Make sure you beat the cake mixture thoroughly to incorporate air.

Sweet scones

These scones are very airy, light and delicious.

Makes 24 scones

1 oz/25 g golden linseeds

6 oz/150 g brown rice flour

4 oz/100 g potato flour

1 tsp bread (baking) soda

4 oz/100 g millet flake (the finer the better)

2 oz/50 g rice bran

a small pinch of salt

2 oz/50 g sugar

4 oz/100 g/1 stick/½ cup butter

2 eggs

¾ pint/375 ml/1¾ cups buttermilk (see method for quantity)

sesame seeds to sprinkle (optional)

Grind the linseeds or soak them in one-third of the buttermilk and leave for 2–3 hours or overnight. If you are grinding them just add the ground linseeds as one of the dry ingredients.

Pre-heat the oven to 425°F/220°C/Gas 7. Sieve the flour and soda into a bowl. Add the other dry ingredients (including the ground linseed if appropriate) and mix well. Rub the butter into the mixture.

Now add the liquid ingredients (including the soaked linseed and the liquid if appropriate) and mix well. Care should be taken to get the right consistency so don't add all the buttermilk at once. The resulting mix should be too stiff to pour but too liquid to knead (slightly wetter than queen cake mixture).

Spoon the mixture into well-oiled non-stick queen cake tins using a dessert spoon. Sprinkle the tops with sesame seeds and bake in the preheated oven for 20–25 minutes.

Variations

Add washed dried fruit of your choice and a little orange zest to the scone mixture before baking.

Add cubes of peeled and cored cooking apple to the scone mixture and sprinkle the tops of the scones with brown sugar before baking.

Savoury potato scones

These are best baked in greased muffin or queencake tins. If you use potatoes other than Golden Wonders, you will most likely need less buttermilk. The batter should be like queen cake mixture.

Makes 8–10 muffin size or 16–20
    queen cake size scones

2 dstsp golden linseeds

10 fl oz/250 ml/2½ cup buttermilk

6oz/150g brown rice flour

2oz/50g millet flake

8 oz/200 g mashed potato

pinch of salt

1 level tsp bread soda (baking soda)

2 tblsp olive oil

Soak the linseeds in the buttermilk for a few hours or overnight or grind them finely. Preheat the oven to 220°C/425°F/Gas 7.

Mix the rice flour, millet, potato, salt, ground linseeds (if not soaked) and the soda and the oil. Gradually add the buttermilk or the linseed and buttermilk mixture and mix well. Spoon it into the prepared tins and bake in the preset oven for about 35–40 minutes—the bottoms get quite brown and crisp when done.

Variations

For richer scones use an egg and cut down on the amount of buttermilk used. For herb scones simply add 3–4 tablespoons of fresh chopped herbs to the mix before baking. Chives always give a good flavour and can be used on their own or in combination with other herbs.

Mini yeast breads

Of all my recipes for bread, this one is my mother's favourite. I think that you will find these little breads delicious.

Makes about 6 mini-breads

½ oz/10 g golden linseeds

1 tsp dried yeast

½ tsp sugar

4 oz/100 g brown rice flour

2 oz/50 g soya flour

1 oz/25 g rice bran

½ tsp salt

½ oz/10 g butter

7 fl oz/175 ml/¾ cup warm water (generous)

1 large egg, beaten

sesame seeds or poppy seeds (optional)

Grind the linseeds or soak them in the water for 2–3 hours or overnight. Before using this mixture place the container in a bowl of boiling water for 3–4 minutes so that the linseed mixture comes up to blood heat. If you are using ground linseeds just add them to the dry ingredients and use warm water to mix.

Place the dry ingredients in a bowl. Rub in the butter and then stir in the linseed mixture or the warm water if the linseeds have been ground. Stir in the beaten egg. Mix well to blend. The mixture should be a little bit looser than cake mixture. If it's too dry just add a little more warm water.

Transfer the mixture to well-oiled non-stick muffin or queen cake tins. Cover with a plastic bag and leave to prove in a warm place. When the dough has risen to or above the surface of the tins, sprinkle them with the sesame or poppy seeds if desired.

Place the tins in a preheated oven 230°C/450°F/Gas 8 for about 15 minutes. When they leave the sides of the tins and when a skewer inserted into the centre comes out clean the breads are done. Remove them from the tins while hot. (You may need to use a knife for this, though if you have very good tins they will just fall out.) Place on a wire tray to cool.

This mixture is equally good cooked in a loaf tin, greased and bottom-lined with parchment paper: just double the quantity and allow the mixture to rise to the top of the tin before baking. (Bake the mixture as bread at a lower temperature 190ºC/375ºF/Gas 5. It should take 50–60 minutes.)

Date and pecan bread with molasses

This bread is a real winner. The molasses, rich in iron and calcium, gives it a hint of sweetness making it the perfect accompaniment to cheese. To measure the molasses, heat the dessertspoon first either in boiling water or in a gas flame and the molasses will fall off the spoon easily. The loaf is packed with nourishment, is high in fibre and tastes delicious!

1 oz/25 g golden linseeds

19 fl oz/475 ml/generous 2¼ cups buttermilk

6 oz/150 g brown rice flour

4 oz/100 g potato flour

1 (rounded) tsp bread (baking) soda

2 oz/50 g millet flakes

2 oz/50 g rice bran

1 oz/25 g sesame seeds

1 tsp salt

2 oz/50 g chopped dates

2 oz/50 g chopped pecans

3 tblsp olive oil

1 dstsp molasses

Grind the linseeds finely or soak them for 2–3 hours or overnight in the buttermilk.

Preheat the oven to 190°C/375°F/Gas 5. Sift the flour and bread (baking) soda. Mix all the dry ingredients together including the ground linseeds (if appropriate).

Stir in the buttermilk (or the buttermilk and linseed mixture if using), the olive oil and the molasses. The batter in this recipe is quite loose (runny).

Grease and bottom-line a loaf tin with parchment paper. Transfer the mixture to the tin. Cover with a sheet of foil (to prevent the crust from getting too dark and dry) and bake in the preheated oven for 1½ hours.

Test with a metal skewer to check that it is cooked in the middle.

Turn out onto a wire tray to cool.

Potato and rice flour bread with linseeds

This white bread has all the goodness of rice flour, rice bran and linseeds and is perfect for slicing. Of all the recipes this is probably the one which most closely resembles 'ordinary' bread.

1 oz/25 g golden linseeds	6 oz/150 g rice flour
1 tsp salt	1 oz/25 g rice bran
1 tsp dried yeast	11 fl oz/275 ml/generous 1¼ cups
1 tsp sugar	warm water
6 oz/150 g potato flour	3 tblsp olive oil

Grind the linseeds finely or soak them for 2–3 hours or overnight in the water. Grease and bottom-line a loaf tin with parchment paper. Mix the ground linseeds with all the dry ingredients. (If you are soaking the linseeds in water, stand the container in a container of boiling water until the linseed mixture is warm. Then add this to the dry ingredients together with the olive oil.)

Add the warm water and olive oil and mix well—the mixture should be just soft enough to pour easily. Pour the mixture into the tin.

Place the tin in a warm place, covering it loosely with a plastic bag. Leave it until the mixture rises to double its size.

Preheat the oven to 190°C/375°F/Gas 5. Bake the bread for about 50 minutes. Test with a metal skewer to ensure that it is done in the middle. Turn it out onto a wire tray to cool.

Rice and millet soda bread

This is a lovely soft bread with a soft golden brown crust. It rises as well as any wheaten soda bread and to my mind is just as delicious. It cuts well and toasts well from the freezer. You could use this mixture for scones too, simply by placing the mixture in very well-oiled queen cake or muffin tins instead of a loaf tin.

Makes 1 loaf

1 oz/25 g golden linseeds

13 fl oz/325 ml/generous 1 ½ cups buttermilk

3 oz/75 g potato flour

6 oz/150 g rice flour

3 oz/75 g millet flake (the finer the better)

1 oz/25 g rice bran

1 tsp salt

1 tsp bread soda (baking soda)

1 egg

3 tblsp olive oil

Grind the linseeds finely or soak them for 2–3 hours or overnight in the buttermilk.

Preheat the oven to 190°C/375°F/Gas 5. Grease and bottom-line a loaf tin with parchment paper.

Sieve the flours into a bowl. Add the other dry ingredients and the ground linseeds, if using, and mix well. Add the egg and oil, the soaked linseeds (if using the soaking method) and most of the buttermilk and mix well. Add the rest of the buttermilk or enough to make a thick batter. (Sometimes the mix may take more liquid than at other times depending on the absorbency of the dry ingredients.) The mixture should be soft enough to pour into the tin (a bit wetter than queen cake mixture).

Bake for about 1 hour. Test with a metal skewer to ensure that it is done in the middle. If it is getting too brown during the course of baking, cover it with a sheet of foil. Turn out onto a wire tray to cool.

Corn bread

This bread is excellent eaten warm or on the day it is made. It rises well and cuts well and can be frozen. Toast it lightly before eating, if you are using it from the freezer.

Makes 1 loaf

3 dstsp golden linseeds

18 fl oz/450 ml/2¼ cups buttermilk

10 oz/250 g medium cornmeal/
   maizemeal

1½ tsp bread (baking) soda

3 oz/75 g brown rice flour

1 oz/25 g rice bran

½ tsp salt

1 egg

1 tblsp olive oil

Grind the linseeds finely or soak them for 2–3 hours or overnight in the buttermilk.

Preheat the oven to 200°C/400°F/Gas 6. Grease and bottom-line a loaf tin with parchment paper.

Mix all the dry ingredients together in a mixing bowl. Beat the egg and stir it into the buttermilk and linseed mixture (or into the buttermilk, if you are using the ground linseeds) together with the olive oil. Now add the liquid mixture to the dry ingredients and stir well. The mix should be quite wet, like a thick batter. Pour the batter into the prepared loaf tin. Bake it for about 45 minutes until the bread is firm to the touch and a skewer inserted into it comes out clean.

Pizza base

This is a win, win, pizza base as there is no rolling involved and it tastes delicious too!

2 tblsp olive oil

8 fl ozs/200 ml/1 cup warm water

1 tsp unrefined caster (super fine) sugar

½ sachet/7 g/1 tsp dried yeast

4 oz/100 g potato flour

4 oz/100 g brown rice flour

1 oz/25 g rice bran

small pinch salt

Mix the olive oil, water, sugar and yeast together in a small bowl and leave to bubble up for about 10 minutes in a warm place. Mix the rest of the ingredients together in a mixing bowl. Add the yeast mixture to the dry ingredients and stir well. The mixture should be too wet to roll out. Place the mixture on a greased non-stick pizza plate, 10 in/24 cm diameter, or any non-stick baking tray and flatten it out with a spatula or spoon. Place the plate in a warm place until the mixture reaches the top of the pizza plate. Meanwhile, preheat the oven to 230°C/450°F/Gas 8.

Bake the pizza base. It will only take about 10 minutes. Test to see if it is cooked through by inserting a skewer into the base at an angle. If it comes out clean, the base is done. It should also leave the sides of the tin and lift off easily from the base when done. Complete the pizza with your favourite toppings and return to the oven to finish cooking.

Savoury pastry (pie dough) without egg

3 oz/75 g potato flour

3 oz/75 g soya flour

6 oz/150 g rice flour

1 oz/25 g linseeds, milled finely in a
    food processor or liquidiser

6 oz/150 g/1½ sticks/¾ cup butter

Sift the flours together into a bowl. Add the linseeds. Cut the butter into cubes and using the tips of the fingers, rub it into the flour mixture. Add water to bind. More water will be needed than would be required for the same quantity of wheaten pastry (pie dough)—it should be ever so slightly sticky. It will roll quite well immediately.

Cornflour (maize flour) sponge cake

3 eggs

3 oz/75 g caster (super fine) sugar

3 oz/75 g cornflour (maize flour)

½ tsp wheat-/gluten-free baking powder

Preheat the oven to 220°C/425°F/Gas 7. Grease two 6–7 in/15–18 cm sandwich tins, bottom-line them with parchment paper, grease again and dust with cornflour.

Beat the eggs and the sugar together with a whisk or electric mixer until the whisk leaves a trail in the mixture and it is thick and mousse-like. Now fold in the sifted flour and baking powder and transfer the mixture into the cake tins. Bake in the oven for about 20 minutes. The cake is done when it is springy to the touch and it leaves the sides of the tin.

Turn out onto a wire tray to cool. When cold, fill with whipped cream or crème fraîche and home-made jam, fruit spread or fresh fruit.

Rice flour sponge cake

3 eggs

2 oz/50 g unrefined caster (super fine) sugar

3 oz/75 g brown rice flour

½ tsp wheat-/gluten-free baking powder

Preheat the oven to 220°C/425°F/Gas 7. Grease two 6–7 in/15–18 cm sandwich tins, bottom-line them with parchment paper, grease again and dust with rice flour. Beat the eggs and the sugar together with a whisk or electric mixer until the whisk leaves a trail in the mixture and it is thick and mousse-like. Now fold in the sifted flour and baking powder and transfer the mixture into the cake tins. Bake in the oven for about 20 minutes. The cake is done when it is springy to the touch and it leaves the sides of the tin.

Turn out onto a wire tray to cool. When cold, fill with whipped cream or crème fraîche and home-made jam, fruit spread or fresh fruit.

Fresh strawberry gateau

1 punnet fresh strawberries, hulled, washed and dried

1 rice flour sponge cake

home-made strawberry jam

strawberry or almond liqueur (optional)

1 medium carton fresh cream, whipped

Reserve a few strawberries for decoration and mash the remainder. If using a liqueur sprinkle a little of it over the sponge cake. Cover the bottom sponge cake with jam. Place one third of the cream mixed with the mashed strawberries on top of the jam. Spread jam on the second sponge cake and place it on top of the cream. Decorate the top with the remaining whipped cream and the reserved hulled strawberries.

Variation

To vary the flavour use different kinds of fruits, jams, liqueurs, flavoured butter creams or cream. When using stewed fruit, e.g. apricot, moisten the sponge with some of the cooking liquid or use a mixture of the stewing liquid and liqueur. Try to match the fruit to the jam but this is not absolutely necessary.

Birthday cake or fairy cakes

This is a very simple recipe, made in a jiffy, requiring the minimum of ingredients to make birthday cakes or little buns. You can change the flavour by substituting another flavouring for the vanilla e.g. orange or lemon zest or coffee. To make a chocolate cake simply omit 2 oz/50 g flour and substitute cocoa powder instead. To make a coffee cake dissolve a teaspoon of instant coffee in just enough hot water to make a paste of the grains and add it to the cake mixture. No matter what flavour cake you are making, it is important to beat the mixture until it is very light and fluffy. This incorporates air which helps the cake to rise.

3 eggs

6 oz/150 g/1½ sticks/¾ cup butter

4 oz/100 g unrefined caster (super fine) sugar

6 oz/150 g brown rice flour, sifted

2 level tsp wheat-/gluten-free baking powder

1 tsp natural vanilla essence/extract (optional)

Put all the ingredients in the bowl of the mixer and beat at high speed until the mixture is very light and fluffy.

For fairy cakes preheat the oven to 190°C/375°F/Gas 5. Spoon the mixture into cake cases and bake until done. The fairy cakes can be eaten as they are or decorated as desired with water icing, butter icing, jam, fruit, cream, crème fraîche, fruit spread etc.

For a Victoria sandwich or birthday cake preheat the oven to 190°C/375°F/Gas 5. Grease two 6–7 in/15–18 cm sandwich tins and bottom-line with parchment paper. Divide the mixture between the tins and bake in the preheated oven for 40–45 minutes. The cake is done when it is springy to the touch and it leaves the sides of the tin. Turn it out onto a wire tray to cool.

To fill the birthday cake use fruit spread, jam, buttercream or whipped cream and to decorate it use water icing, buttercream or whipped cream.

Marmalade cake

This is a cake with a delicious orange flavour. It will keep well in a tin for about a week. However, it is so delicious I doubt if it will last that long!

8 oz/200 g/2 sticks/1 cup butter

4 oz/100 g unrefined caster (super fine) sugar

zest of one small orange

3 tblsp marmalade

4 small or 3 large eggs

5 oz/125 g brown rice flour, sifted

3 oz/75 g cornflour or maize flour, sifted

2 tsp wheat/gluten-free baking powder

Preheat the oven to 200°C/400°F/Gas 6. Grease and bottom-line a loaf-tin with parchment paper.

Beat the butter, sugar, orange zest and marmalade together on high speed. Add the eggs and flour and baking powder. Continue to beat on high speed until the mixture is very light and fluffy. Pour into the loaf tin. If there is too much mixture, you can make a few queen cakes with the rest. Bake in the preheated oven. The cake is done when golden brown, springy to the touch and leaving the sides of the tin. Test with a metal skewer to check that it is cooked in the middle. Gently turn it out onto a wire tray to cool.

Chocolate fudge cake

For the cake

5 oz/125 g brown rice flour

1½ oz/35 g cocoa powder

3 eggs

6 oz/150 g/1½ sticks/¾ cup butter

4 oz/100 g unrefined caster (super fine) sugar

2 level tsp wheat-/gluten-free baking powder

Preheat the oven to 190°C/375°F/Gas 5. Grease two 6–7 inch/15–18 cm sandwich tins and bottom-line them with parchment paper.

Sift the flour, cocoa powder and baking powder together. Place all the ingredients in a mixer bowl and beat. Now increase the speed to high and beat until the mixture is very airy and light.

Divide the mixture between the tins and bake in the preheated oven until it leaves the sides of the tin and is springy to the touch (about 35 minutes). Turn out onto a wire tray to cool.

For the filling

1 oz/25 g/¼ stick/2 tblsp butter	2 tblsp milk
2 oz/50 g plain (semi-sweet) chocolate	6 oz/150 g icing (confectioner's) sugar

Place the butter, chocolate and milk in a bowl and place the bowl over hot water. Do not allow the water to boil. Remove the bowl from over the hot water as soon as the chocolate is melted. Stir only when the chocolate has melted. Now add the sugar and beat well. Fill the cake with this mixture.

Chocolate and prune gateau

Fill a chocolate fudge cake with chocolate and prune filling (below).

4 oz/100 g prunes	2 oz/50 g suitable dark or milk choco- late
1 oz/25 g/¼ stick/2 tblsp butter	1 oz/25 g icing (confectioner's) sugar

Cook the prunes in water without sugar. Drain them, remove the stones (pits), and whizz them in a food processor or liquidiser. Put them in a bowl with the butter and chocolate. Place the bowl over a saucepan of barely simmering water. Do not disturb the contents of the bowl until all the chocolate and butter has melted completely.

Remove the bowl from the heat. Whisk in the sugar. Leave the filling to cool slightly before filling and decorating the chocolate cake.

Lemon cake with lemon date filling

The filling is a buttercream filling made with dates instead of sugar. To vary the cake and its filling, make it with orange instead of lemon. If you wish to cover the top of the cake as well as filling it, you will need to double the quantity.

For the cake

3 eggs

6 oz/150 g/1½ sticks/¾ cup butter

5 oz/125 g brown rice flour, sifted

1 oz/25 g maizeflour or cornflour, sifted

3 oz/75 g unrefined caster (super fine) sugar

zest of ½ lemon

2 level tsp wheat-/gluten-free baking powder

Preheat the oven to 190°C/375°F/Gas 5. Grease two 6–7 in/15–18 cm sandwich tins and bottom-line them with parchment paper.

Beat all the ingredients together until light and fluffy. Divide the mixture between the tins and bake in the preheated oven until the cake leaves the sides of the tin and is springy to the touch (about 30–35 minutes).

Turn out onto a wire tray to cool.

For the filling

4 oz/100 g dried pressed dates, stoned (pitted) and chopped

zest and juice of ½ lemon

2–3 tblsp water

1 oz/25 g/¼ stick/2 tblsp butter at room temperature

Put the dates with the lemon zest, juice and water in a saucepan. Place the saucepan over low heat. The hot liquid soon begins to dissolve the dates. Beat with a wooden spoon to form a stiff puree. (You might need to add a little more water if the dates are very dry and hard.) If you add too much water you can just boil it off again.

Allow the mixture to cool and add the softened butter. Beat until smooth and use to fill the cake.

Carob, almond and orange cake

For the cake

6 oz/150 g/1½ sticks/¾ cup butter

6 oz/150 g unrefined caster (super fine) sugar

5 oz/125 g brown rice flour, sifted

1 oz/25 g carob powder, sifted

½ oz/35 g ground almonds

3 eggs

2 level tsp wheat-/gluten-free baking powder

½ tsp natural almond essence (extract)

½ tsp natural vanilla essence (extract)

Preheat the oven to 190°C/375°F/Gas 5. Grease two 6–7 in/15–18 cm sandwich tins and bottom-line them with parchment paper.

Beat all the ingredients together until light and fluffy. Divide the mixture between the tins and bake in the preheated oven until the cake leaves the sides of the tin and is springy to the touch (about 30–35 minutes). Turn out onto a wire tray to cool.

For the filling

1 rounded dstsp carob powder

4 oz/100 g icing (confectioner's) sugar

2 oz/50 g/½ stick/¼ cup butter

zest of ½ orange

orange juice to mix

Sieve together the carob powder and icing (confectioner's) sugar.

Beat the butter until it is light and fluffy. Add the orange zest and beat well. Beat in the sugar and carob mixture and add enough orange juice to achieve the desired consistency.

Sandwich the two cakes together with half of the filling and decorate the top with the other half.

Orange and chocolate chip gateau

For the cake

1 oz/25 g maize flour or cornflour

5 oz/125 g rice flour

2 level tsp wheat-/gluten-free baking
  powder

3 eggs

6 oz/150 g/1 ½ sticks/¾ cup butter

4 oz/100 g unrefined caster (super
  fine) sugar

zest of 1 small orange

2 oz/60 g bar chocolate, chopped into
  small pieces

Preheat the oven to 190°C/375°F/Gas 5. Grease and bottom line two 6–7 inch/
15–18 cm sandwich tins.

Sieve the flours and the baking powder, then mix all the ingredients, except the
chocolate pieces, together. Beat at the highest speed until the mixture is very
fluffy and light. Fold in the chocolate pieces.

Divide the mixture between the greased sandwich tins. Bake until the cake is
golden brown, is springy to the touch and is leaving the sides of the tin (about
30–35 minutes). Turn out onto a wire tray to cool.

For the filling

2 oz/50 g/½ stick/¼ cup butter

4 oz/100 g icing (confectioner's) sugar,
  sifted

zest and juice of 1 small orange

Combine the butter, sugar and orange zest, adding enough orange juice to achieve
the desired consistency. Beat until fluffy and use to fill and decorate the top of
the cake. If desired, sprinkle the top with grated chocolate.

Carrot cake

For the cake

4 oz/100 g brown rice flour

1 oz/25 g cornflour

1½ tsp wheat-/gluten-free baking
  powder

2 eggs

3 oz/75 g brown sugar

4 oz/100 g/1 stick/½ cup butter

½ tsp ground cinnamon

½ tsp ground nutmeg

½ tsp ground ginger

½ tsp ground clove

1 medium carrot, peeled and grated

Preheat the oven to 190°C/375°F/Gas 5. Grease and bottom-line a loaf tin. with parchment paper.

Sieve the flours and baking powder together. Place all the ingredients, except the carrot, in your mixer bowl and beat at high speed until the mixture is light and fluffy. Finally, mix in the carrot.

Bake in the preheated oven for approximately 45 minutes or until the cake is firm to the touch and leaves the sides of the tin.

Serve with natural organic yogurt flavoured with lemon zest, lemon juice and honey. Alternatively, top with the mixture below.

For the topping

2 oz/50 g sifted icing sugar (confectioner's sugar)

1 oz/25 g cream cheese

zest and juice of ½ a lemon

Combine the cheese, sugar and lemon zest and enough juice to achieve the desired consistency. Beat well and use to top the cake.

Fruity buckwheat buns

These buns are delicious hot out of the oven, split open and served with butter.
When cold they tend to become very hard. There is no need to resort to the sledge-
hammer, however, as reheating softens them!

Makes 14–15 buns

5 oz/125 g buckwheat flour

5 oz/125 g brown rice flour

5 oz/125 g potato flour

2 oz/50 g/½ stick/¼ cup butter

1 egg

½ pint/250 ml/1¼ cups buttermilk

2 oz/50 g unrefined brown sugar

½ tsp ground nutmeg

zest of 1 orange

1½ tsp bread (baking) soda

2 oz/50 g currants

2 oz/50 g sultanas (golden raisins)

Preheat the oven to 200°C/400°F/Gas 6.

Sieve all the flours together. Rub in the butter. Beat the egg and milk and add with the remaining ingredients to the flour mixture and mix well. With floured hands (rice flour) shape the mixture into balls (about 14 or 15 in total).

Place them on a greased baking tray. Flatten them slightly with the hands and bake them for 20–25 minutes.

Rice and almond cookies

These make excellent treats for the wheat-/gluten-free lunch box.

Makes 12 cookies

2 oz/50 g/½ stick/¼ cup butter

3¾ oz/90 g unrefined caster (superfine) sugar

1 oz/25 g rice bran

2½ oz/60 g brown rice flour

¼ tsp baking powder

3 oz/75 g ground almonds

½ tsp vanilla essence (extract)

1 egg

Preheat the oven to 180°C/350°F/Gas 4.

Cream the butter and sugar. Add all the other ingredients and mix well. Shape into balls with the hands. Place on a greased baking tin and flatten a little. Bake in the preheated oven for about 20 minutes.

Date slices

The dates are cooked to a spreadable mixture with the water and lemon and this mixture is sandwiched between two crumbly layers. Sometimes the dried dates are so dry that it will take more water than the recipe suggests to make them soft. Just use your discretion and add more if needs be. If you add too much water just cook it off in the saucepan. The slices can also be served with egg custard (page 174) as a dessert. You will need a Swiss roll tin about 8½ in x12½ in/22 x 32 cm.

Makes 16 slices

12 oz/300 g dates, pitted and chopped

6 tblsp water

grated zest and juice of 1 lemon

6 oz/150 g/1½ sticks/¾ cup butter

4 dstsp maple syrup *or* 3 dstsp unrefined caster (superfine) sugar

4 oz/100 g millet flakes

6 oz/150 g brown rice flour

2 oz/50 g pecan nuts, ground

Preheat the oven to 200°C/400°F/Gas 6. Grease the Swiss roll tin.

Place the dates in a saucepan with the water, lemon zest and juice. Heat the mixture gently and stir occasionally until the mixture is soft. Remove from the heat.

In another saucepan heat the butter until just melted and add the syrup or sugar. In a bowl combine the flakes, flour and ground pecan nuts (use a food processor to grind the nuts). Pour the melted butter mixture into the dry mixture and stir. Place half of the crumbly mixture on the base of the tin, flatten it and press it down with the back of a tablespoon.

Place the date mixture on top spreading it gently over the crumbly mixture. Cover the date mixture with the rest of the crumbly mixture and again press it down gently.

Bake in the pre-set oven for about 20 minutes. Cool in the tin and cut into 16 slices.

Almond macaroons

Makes about 12 macaroons

2–3 egg whites (depends on size)

4 oz/100 g ground almonds

4 oz/100 g unrefined caster (super fine) sugar

1 oz/25 g maize flour/cornflour

1 oz/25 g brown rice flour

½ tsp natural almond essence (extract)

whole almonds to decorate

Preheat the oven to 180°C/350°F/Gas 4.

Lightly whip the egg whites. Mix the dry ingredients together. Add enough of the egg white to the dry mixture to make a soft paste. Add in the almond essence (extract) and mix again.

Using floured hands (rice flour), shape the mixture into 12 small balls. Place them on a baking sheet. Flatten them slightly and insert an almond into the centre of each.

Bake for about 20–25 minutes or until golden brown.

Boiled fruit cake

Wash dried fruit in warm water and dry it in a clean tea towel before use.

6 oz/150 g raisins, washed and dried

6 oz/150 g sultanas (golden raisins), washed and dried

6 oz/150 g currants, washed and dried

½ pint/250 ml/1¼ cup water

4 oz/100 g/1 stick/½ cup butter

4 oz/100 g Muscovado *or* Barbados sugar

2 tblsp golden linseeds, crushed finely

3 free range eggs

10 oz/250 g brown rice flour

2 tsp gluten-free/wheat-free baking powder

1 tsp freshly grated nutmeg

2 tblsp marmalade

1 oz/25 g chopped nuts

2 oz/50 g natural glace cherries (not coloured), washed to remove the syrup

2 oz/50 g mixed peel

Preheat the oven to 180°C/350°F/Gas 4. Line a 9 in/22 cm round cake tin with greaseproof or parchment paper.

Put the fruit in a saucepan with the water, butter, and sugar. Heat gently until the butter has melted. Then remove the mixture from the heat and allow it to cool for about 30 minutes.

Add the rest of the ingredients. Pour the mixture into the prepared tin and bake in the preheated oven for about 2 hours or until a skewer inserted into the cake comes out clean. Allow the cake to cool in the tin.

After about 30 minutes you could pour a little brandy or rum over it. This is optional.

The cake will keep well for a week or two in an airtight tin wrapped in greaseproof or parchment paper. Use a sharp serrated knife to cut it as wheat-/gluten-free fruit cakes are very delicate and break up easily.

Christmas cake

It was all hands on deck for the Christmas baking when I was a child. Some of you who like me, are twenty-one and a huge bit, will remember blanching and peeling the almonds before grinding them, or soaking the large, luscious Valentia raisins before removing the pips (seeds). The eggs for the baking came from the earthenware crock where they had been preserved in waterglass from their summer abundance.

Christmas baking today is so easy and convenient by comparison. No matter how convenient the fruit might be however, it still needs to be washed and dried to remove any dirt and/or oil. Wash it in warm water, drain it in a colander or sieve and dry it in a clean tea towel. Spread it out on a baking tray and place in a cool oven to dry.

As with all ingredients organic is best. Failing that, buy the best possible quality you can. Use Muscovado or Barbados sugar for the best flavour. Try to get the old-fashioned candied peel or at least peel which does not have colouring. Avoid the brightly coloured cherries. Get the natural ones instead. If the cherries are very gooey, rinse them in warm water and dry them with a clean tea towel.

The method here is unusual for a Christmas cake but it gives the best results. It is best to make the cake not more than two weeks before Christmas as like all fruit cakes which are wheat-/gluten-free it becomes more crumbly with age.

For the cake

8 oz/200g sultanas (golden raisins), washed and dried

8 oz/200g raisins, washed and dried

4 oz/100g dates, stoned (pitted)

4 oz/100 g glace cherries

2 oz/50 g candied peel

2 tblsp brandy or dark rum

6 oz/150 g/1½ sticks/¾ cup butter

5 oz/125 g rice flour

1 oz/25 g maize flour

2 oz/50 g rice bran

½ grated nutmeg

2 oz/50 g ground almonds

6 oz/150 g unrefined dark brown sugar

grated zest and juice of ½ lemon

8 oz/200g grated cooking apple

4 large eggs, beaten

Soak the fruit overnight in the brandy or rum.

Line an 8 in/20 cm round cake tin or a 7 in/18 cm square tin with a double thickness of greaseproof or parchment paper and also put a strip of cardboard around the outside of the tin, securing it with cotton string.

Preheat the oven to 160°C/325°F/Gas 3. Melt the butter slowly in a saucepan over low heat. Sift the flour and mix all the dry ingredients together. Add the grated lemon zest and juice and the grated apple to the soaked fruit. Add the dry ingredients, then the beaten eggs and finally the melted butter. Mix well.

Transfer the mixture to the prepared cake tin. Smooth the top. Cover it with a double thickness of greaseproof or parchment paper and bake it for the first hour at 160°C/325°F/Gas 3.

Remove the paper and turn the heat down to 140°C/250°F/Gas 1 for about 2 hours more. Test with a skewer to see if it is done. The skewer will come out clean if the cake is done right through.

Allow the cake to cool in the tin. Pour some brandy or rum over it. When it is completely cold do not remove the paper from around it but wrap it in more greaseproof or parchment paper and place it in a biscuit tin. Store it in a cool place.

For the almond paste

5 oz/125 g icing (confectioner's) sugar, 1 tblsp lemon juice
   sifted 2 tblsp brandy
10 oz/ 250 g ground almonds ½ tsp natural vanilla essence
5 oz/125 g unrefined caster (superfine) ½ tsp natural almond essence
   sugar apricot jam
1 fresh organic or free range egg

Place the dry ingredients in a bowl and mix them together. Beat the egg in another bowl and add the liquid ingredients to it. Pour the liquid into the dry ingredients and mix well. Knead the mixture with your hands.

Brush the top and sides of the cake with the warmed jam. Roll the almond paste out to the correct size. Place the almond paste over the cake and allow it to drape down over the sides. Mould it in place with your hands and trim if necessary.

For the royal icing

I no longer ice my Christmas cake as it just adds more sugar to the diet at a time when too much sugar is already being consumed. If you want to ice it, the most convenient way is to buy instant royal icing and follow the packet instructions. If you would like the icing to remain soft just add a teaspoon of glycerine to it–you can buy glycerine in any pharmacy.

Further reading

The following books have been of great help to me in regaining my health, deepening my spirituality, living joyfully, and growing in consciousness and understanding. I give thanks for the authors and their works as I share them with you.

Bach, Edward *Heal Thyself* C. W. Daniel, London 1991

Beattie, Melody *Beyond Codependency How to Stop Controlling Others and Start Caring for Yourself* Hazelden Foundation Europe, PO Box 616, Cork, Ireland 1989

—*Codependent No More* Hazelden Foundation Europe, PO Box 616, Cork, Ireland

Callan, Dawn *Awakening The Warrior Within* Tenacity Press, California 1999

Carlson, Richard *You Can Be Happy No Matter What* Hodder and Stoughton, London 1997

Chopra, Deepak *The Seven Spiritual Laws of Success—A practical guide to the fulfilment of your dreams* Bantam Press, London 1996

De Mello, Anthony *Awareness* Harper Collins, London 1990

Dyer Dr Wayne W. *Your Erroneous Zones* Harper Collins, New York 1977

—*Pulling Your Own Strings* Harper Collins, New York 1978

—*Your Sacred Self—Making the Decision to be Free* Harper Collins, New York 1996

Hartmann, Thom *The Last Hours of Ancient Sunlight—Waking up to personal and global transformation* Three Rivers Press, New York 2000

Hay, Louise L. *You Can Heal Your Life* Eden Grove Editions, London 1984

Kennedy, Stanislaus *Now Is The Time* Town House and Country House, Dublin 1998

Morgan, Marlo *Mutant Message Down Under* Thorsons/Harper Collins, London 1994

Myss, Caroline *Anatomy of the Spirit The Seven Stages of Power and Healing* Bantam Books, London 1998

—*Why People Don't Heal and How They Can* Three Rivers New York 1997

Northrup, Christiane *Women's Bodies, Women's Wisdom The Complete Guide to Women's Health and Wellbeing* Piatkus London 1999

Roman, Sanaya *Living With Joy* H. J. Kramer California 1986

Roman, Sanaya *Personal Power Through Awareness* H. J. Kramer California 1986

Shin, Shovel *The Game of Life and How To Play It* C W Daniel London

Siegal, Bernie S. *Peace, Love and Healing* Arrow London 1990

Stauffer, Edith R *Unconditional Love and Forgiveness* Triangle Publishers, California:1988

The Quiet Mind White Eagle Publishing Hampshire 1994

The Source Of All Our Strength White Eagle Publishing Hampshire 1996

Zukav, Garry *Soul Stories* Random House London 2000

Recommended reading on food safety

Carson, Rachel *Silent Spring* London: Penguin 1965

Colborn, Theo, Dumanoski Dianne and Meyers, John Peterson *Our Stolen Future, Are We Threatening Our Fertility, Intelligence and Survival? A Scientific Detective Story* Abacus, Little Brown, London1996

Erasmus, Udo *Fats that Heal, Fats that Kill* Alive Books, Canada 1986, 1993

Hird, Vicki *Perfectly Safe to Eat?* The Women's Press Lonson 2000

Porritt, Jonathan *Playing Safe: Science and the Environment* London: Thames and Hudson

Tatlow, Maureen *Good Enough To Eat?* Gill and Macmillan, London 1998

Coeliac societies

The Coeliac Society of Ireland (www.geocities.com/hotsprings/resort/60051)

Carmichael House, 4 North Brunswick Street, Dublin 2, Ireland

This is a wonderful voluntary organisation providing information and support to those who suffer from coeliac disease The society produces and regularly updates a pocket guide to gluten-free manufactured products and distributes it to its members.

Tel 01-872 1471

Other Coeliac societies include:

The Coeliac Society of Great Britain (www.coeliac.co.uk)

PO Box 220, High Wycombe, Buckinghamshire, HP11 2HY, England

The Canadian Coeliac Association (www.celiac.ca/eframes.htm)

190 Britannia Road E., Unit 11, Mississauga, Ontario LZA 1W6, Canada

The Coeliac Society of South Africa

C/o Mrs M Kaplan, 91 Third Avenue, Percelia 2192, Johannesburg, South Africa

American Coeliac Society (www.healthfinder.gov/test/orgs/hr1399.htm)

58 Musano Court, West Orange, New Jersey NJ 07052, USA

Index

✓ dairy-free recipes